"Surely it is good to be alive at a time like this."

THE
FRIENDLY ROAD

New Adventures in Contentment

By

DAVID GRAYSON

Author of "Adventures in Contentment,"
"Adventures in Friendship"

Illustrated by
THOMAS FOGARTY

GARDEN CITY   NEW YORK
DOUBLEDAY, PAGE & COMPANY
1913

A WORD TO HIM WHO OPENS
THIS BOOK

I did not plan when I began writing these
chapters to make an entire book, but only to put
down the more or less unusual impressions, the
events and adventures, of certain quiet pilgrimages
in country roads. But when I had written down
all of these things, I found I had material in plenty.

"What shall I call it now that I have written
it?" I asked myself.

At first I thought I should call it "Adventures
on the Road," or "The Country Road," or something equally simple, for I would not have the
title arouse any appetite which the book itself
could not satisfy. One pleasant evening I was
sitting on my porch with my dog sleeping near
me, and Harriet not far away rocking and sewing,
and as I looked out across the quiet fields I could

see in the distance a curving bit of the town road. I could see the valley below it and the green hill beyond, and my mind went out swiftly along the country road which I had so recently travelled on foot, and I thought with deep satisfaction of all the people I had met on my pilgrimages — the Country Minister with his problems, the buoyant Stanleys, Bill Hahn the Socialist, the Vedders in their garden, the Brush Peddler. I thought of the Wonderful City, and of how for a time I had been caught up into its life. I thought of the men I met at the livery stable, especially Healy, the wit, and of that strange Girl of the Street. And it was good to think of them all living around me, not so very far away, connected with me through darkness and space by a certain mysterious human cord. Most of all I love that which I cannot see beyond the hill.

"Harriet," I said aloud, "it grows more wonderful every year how full the world is of friendly people!"

So I got up quickly and came in here to my room, and taking a fresh sheet of paper I wrote down the title of my new book:

"The Friendly Road."

I invite you to travel with me upon this friendly road. You may find, as I did, something which will cause you for a time to forget yourself into contentment. But if you chance to be a truly serious person, put down my book. Let nothing stay your hurried steps, nor keep you from your way.

As for those of us who remain, we will loiter as much as ever we please. We'll take toll of these spring days, we'll stop wherever evening overtakes us, we'll eat the food of hospitality — and make friends for life!

DAVID GRAYSON.

CONTENTS

CONTENTS

ILLUSTRATIONS

I LEAVE MY FARM

CHAPTER I

I LEAVE MY FARM

"Is it so small a thing
To have enjoyed the sun,
To have lived light in spring?"

IT IS eight o'clock of a sunny spring morning. I have been on the road for almost
three hours. At five I left the town of Holt,
before six I had crossed the railroad at a place
called Martin's Landing, and an hour ago, at
seven, I could see in the distance the spires of
Nortontown. And all the morning as I came
tramping along the fine country roads with my
pack-strap resting warmly on my shoulder,
and a song in my throat — just nameless words
to a nameless tune — and all the birds singing,

3

and all the brooks bright under their little bridges, I knew that I must soon step aside and put down, if I could, some faint impression of the feeling of this time and place. I cannot hope to convey any adequate sense of it all — of the feeling of lightness, strength, clearness, I have as I sit here under this maple tree — but I am going to write as long as ever I am happy at it, and when I am no longer happy at it, why, here at my very hand lies the pleasant country road, stretching away toward newer hills and richer scenes.

Until to-day I have not really been quite clear in my own mind as to the step I have taken. My sober friend, have you ever tried to do anything that the world at large considers not quite sensible, not quite sane? Try it! It is easier to commit a thundering crime. A friend of mine delights in walking to town bareheaded, and I fully believe the neighbourhood is more disquieted thereby than it would be if my friend came home drunken or failed to pay his debts.

Here I am then, a farmer, forty miles from home in planting time, taking his ease under a maple tree and writing in a little book held on his knee! Is not that the height of absurdity? Of all my friends the Scotch Preacher was the only one who seemed to understand why it was that I must go away for a time. Oh, I am a sinful and revolutionary person!

When I left home last week, if you could have had a truthful picture of me — for is there not a photography so delicate that it will catch the dim thought-shapes which attend upon our lives? — if you could have had such a truthful picture of me, you would have seen, besides a farmer named Grayson with a gray bag hanging from his shoulder, a strange company following close upon his steps. Among this crew you would have made out easily:

Two fine cows.

Four Berkshire pigs.

One team of gray horses, the old mare a little lame in her right foreleg.

About fifty hens, four cockerels, and a number of ducks and geese.

More than this — I shall offer no explanation in these writings of any miracles that may appear — you would have seen an entirely respectable old farmhouse bumping and hobbling along as best it might in the rear. And in the doorway, Harriet Grayson, in her immaculate white apron, with the veritable look in her eyes which she wears when I am not comporting myself with quite the proper decorum.

Oh, they would not let me go! How they all followed clamoring after me. My thoughts coursed backward faster than ever I could run away. If you could have heard that motley crew of the barnyard as I did — the hens all cackling, the ducks quacking, the pigs grunting, and the old mare neighing and stamping, you would have thought it a miracle that I escaped at all.

So often we think in a superior and lordly manner of our possessions, when, as a matter of fact, we do not really possess them, they possess us. For ten years I have been the humble servant, attending upon the commonest daily needs of sundry hens, ducks, geese, pigs, bees, and of a fussy and exacting old gray mare. And the habit of servitude, I find, has worn deep scars upon me. I am almost like the life prisoner who finds the door of his cell suddenly open, and fears to escape. Why, I had almost become *all* farmer.

On the first morning after I left home I

awoke as usual about five o'clock with the irresistible feeling that I must do the milking. So well disciplined had I become in my servitude that I instinctively thrust my leg out of bed — but pulled it quickly back in again, turned over, drew a long, luxurious breath, and said to myself:

"Avaunt cows! Get thee behind me, swine! Shoo, hens!"

Instantly the clatter of mastery to which I had responded so quickly for so many years grew perceptibly fainter, the hens cackled less domineeringly, the pigs squealed less insistently, and as for the strutting cockerel, that lordly and despotic bird stopped fairly in the middle of a crow, and his voice gurgled away in a spasm of astonishment. As for the old farmhouse, it grew so dim I could scarcely see it at all! Having thus published abroad my Declaration of Independence, nailed my defiance to the door, and otherwise established myself as a free person, I turned over in my bed and took another delicious nap.

Do you know, friend, we can be free of many things that dominate our lives by merely crying out a rebellious "Avaunt!"

But in spite of this bold beginning, I assure

you it required several days to break the habit of cows and hens. The second morning I awakened again at five o'clock, but my leg did not make for the side of the bed; the third morning I was only partially awakened, and on the fourth morning I slept like a millionaire (or at least I slept as a millionaire is supposed to sleep!) until the clock struck seven.

For some days after I left home — and I walked out as casually that morning as though I were going to the barn — I scarcely thought or tried to think of anything but the Road. Such an unrestrained sense of liberty, such an exaltation of freedom, I have not known since I was a lad. When I came to my farm from the city many years ago it was as one bound, as one who had lost out in the world's battle and was seeking to get hold again somewhere upon the realities of life. I have related elsewhere how I thus came creeping like one sore wounded from the field of battle, and how, among our hills, in the hard, steady labour in the soil of the fields, with new and simple friends around me, I found a sort of rebirth or resurrection. I that was worn out, bankrupt both physically and morally, learned to live again. I have achieved something of high happiness in these years, something I know of pure contentment; and I have learned two or three deep and simple things about life: I have learned that happiness is not to be had for the seeking, but comes quietly to him who pauses at his difficult task and looks upward. I have learned that friendship is very simple, and, more than all else, I have learned the lesson of being quiet, of looking out across the meadows and hills, and of trusting a little in God.

And now, for the moment, I am regaining another of the joys of youth — that of the sense of perfect freedom. I made no plans when I left home, I scarcely chose the direction in which I was to travel, but drifted out, as a boy might, into the great busy world. Oh, I have dreamed of that! It seems almost as though, after ten years, I might again really touch the highest joys of adventure!

So I took the Road as it came, as a man takes a woman, for better or worse — I took the Road, and the farms along it, and the sleepy little villages, and the streams from the hillsides — all with high enjoyment. They were good coin in my purse! And when I had

passed the narrow horizon of my acquaint-
anceship, and reached country new to me, it
seemed as though every sense I had began to
awaken. I must have grown dull, unconsciously, in the last years there on my farm.
I cannot describe the eagerness of discovery
I felt at climbing each new hill, nor the long
breath I took at the top of it as I surveyed
new stretches of pleasant countryside.

Assuredly this is one of the royal moments
of all the year — fine, cool, sparkling spring
weather. I think I never saw the meadows
richer and greener — and the lilacs are still
blooming, and the catbirds and orioles are
here. The oaks are not yet in full leaf, but
the maples have nearly reached their full
mantle of verdure — they are very beautiful
and charming to see.

It is curious how at this moment of the year
all the world seems astir. I suppose there is
no moment in any of the seasons when the
whole army of agriculture, regulars and
reserves, is so fully drafted for service in the
fields. And all the doors and windows, both
in the little villages and on the farms, stand
wide open to the sunshine, and all the women
and girls are busy in the yards and gardens.

Such a fine, active, gossipy, adventurous world
as it is at this moment of the year!

It is the time, too, when all sorts of travelling people are afoot.   People who have been

"SUCH A FINE, GOSSIPY WORLD"

mewed up in the cities for the winter now
take to the open road — all the peddlers and
agents and umbrella-menders, all the nursery
salesmen and fertilizer agents, all the tramps
and scientists and poets — all abroad in the

wide sunny roads. They, too, know well this hospitable moment of the spring; they, too, know that doors and hearts are open and that even into dull lives creeps a bit of the spirit of adventure. Why, a farmer will buy a corn planter, feed a tramp, or listen to a poet twice as easily at this time of year as at any other!

For several days I found myself so fully occupied with the bustling life of the Road that I scarcely spoke to a living soul, but strode straight ahead. The spring has been late and cold: most of the corn and some of the potatoes are not yet in, and the tobacco lands are still bare and brown. Occasionally I stopped to watch some ploughman in the fields: I saw with a curious, deep satisfaction how the moist furrows, freshly turned, glistened in the warm sunshine. There seemed to be something right and fit about it, as well as human and beautiful. Or at evening I would stop to watch a ploughman driving homeward across his new brown fields, raising a cloud of fine dust from the fast drying furrow crests. The low sun shining through the dust and glorifying it, the weary-stepping horses, the man all sombre-coloured like the earth itself and knit into the scene as though a part of it, made a picture exquisitely fine to see.

And what a joy I had also of the lilacs blooming in many a dooryard, the odour often trailing after me for a long distance in the road, and of the pungent scent at evening in the cool hollows of burning brush heaps and the smell of barnyards as I went by—not unpleasant, not offensive—and above all, the deep, earthy, moist odour of new-ploughed fields.

And then, at evening, to hear the sound of voices from the dooryards as I pass quite unseen; no words, but just pleasant, quiet intonations of human voices, borne through the still air, or the low sounds of cattle in the barnyards, quieting down for the night, and often, if near a village, the distant, slumbrous sound of a church bell, or even the rumble of a train — how good all these sounds are! They have all come to me again this week with renewed freshness and impressiveness. I am living deep again!

It was not, indeed, until last Wednesday that I began to get my fill, temporarily, of the outward satisfaction of the Road — the primeval takings of the senses — the mere joys of seeing, hearing, smelling, touching.

But on that day I began to wake up; I began to have a desire to know something of all the strange and interestng people who are working in their fields, or standing invitingly in their doorways, or so busily afoot in the country roads. Let me add, also, for this is one of the most important parts of my present experience, that this new desire was far from being wholly esoteric. I had also begun to have cravings which would not in the least be satisfied by landscapes or dulled by the sights and sounds of the road. A whiff here and there from a doorway at mealtime had made me long for my own home, for the sight of Harriet calling from the steps:

"Dinner, David."

But I had covenanted with myself long before starting that I would literally "live light in spring." It was the one and primary condition I made with myself — and made with serious purpose — and when I came away I had only enough money in my pocket and sandwiches in my pack to see me through the first three or four days. Any man may brutally pay his way anywhere, but it is quite another thing to be accepted by your human-kind not as a paid lodger but as a friend.

Always, it seems to me, I have wanted to submit myself, and indeed submit the stranger, to that test. Moreover, how can any man look for true adventure in life if he always knows to a certainty where his next meal is coming from? In a world so completely dominated by goods, by things, by possessions, and smothered by security, what fine adventure is left to a man of spirit save the adventure of poverty?

I do not mean by this the adventure of involuntary poverty, for I maintain that involuntary poverty, like involuntary riches, is a credit to no man. It is only as we dominate life that we really live. What I mean here, if I may so express it, is an adventure in achieved poverty. In the lives of such true men as Francis of Assisi and Tolstoi, that which draws the world to them in secret sympathy is not that they lived lives of poverty, but rather, having riches at their hands, or for the very asking, that they chose poverty as the better way of life.

As for me, I do not in the least pretend to have accepted the final logic of an achieved poverty. I have merely abolished temporarily from my life a few hens and cows, a comfortable old farmhouse, and certain other emoluments and hereditaments — but remain the slave of sundry cloth upon my back and sundry articles in my gray bag — including a fat pocket volume or so, and a tin whistle. Let them pass now. To-morrow I may wish to attempt life with still less. I might survive without my battered copy of "Montaigne" or even submit to existence without that sense of distant companionship symbolized by a postage-stamp, and as for trousers ——

In this deceptive world, how difficult of attainment is perfection!

No, I expect I shall continue for a long time to owe the worm his silk, the beast his hide, the sheep his wool, and the cat his perfume! What I am seeking is something as simple and as quiet as the trees or the hills — just to look out around me at the pleasant countryside, to enjoy a little of this passing show, to meet (and to help a little if I may) a few human beings, and thus to get more nearly into the sweet kernel of human life. My friend, you may or may not think this a worthy object; if you do not, stop here, go no further with me; but if you do, why, we'll exchange great words on the road; we'll look up at the sky together, we'll see and hear the finest things in this world! We'll enjoy the sun! We'll live light in spring!

Until last Tuesday, then, I was carried easily and comfortably onward by the corn, the eggs, and the honey of my past labours, and before Wednesday noon I began to experience in certain vital centres recognizable symptoms of a variety of discomfort anciently familiar to man. And it was all the sharper because I did not know how or where I could assuage it. In all my life, in spite of various ups and downs in a fat world, I don't think I was ever before genuinely hungry. Oh, I've been hungry in a reasonable, civilized way, but I have always known where in an hour or so I could get all I wanted to eat — a condition accountable, in this world, I am convinced, for no end of stupidity. But to be both physically and, let us say, psychologically hungry, and not to know where or how to get anything to eat, adds something to the zest of life.

By noon on Wednesday, then, I was reduced quite to a point of necessity. But where was I to begin, and how? I know from long experience the suspicion with which the ordinary farmer meets the Man of the Road — the man who appears to wish to enjoy the fruits of the earth without working for them with his hands. It is a distrust deep-seated and ages old. Nor can the Man of the Road ever quite understand the Man of the Fields. And here was I, for so long the stationary Man of the Fields, essaying the rôle of the Man of the Road. I experienced a sudden sense of the enlivenment of the faculties: I must now depend upon wit or cunning or human nature to win my way, not upon mere skill of the hand or strength in the bent back. Whereas in my former life, when I was assailed by a Man of the Road, whether tramp or peddler or poet, I had only to stand stock-still within my fences and say nothing — though indeed I never could do that, being far too much interested in every one who came my way — and the invader was soon repelled. There is nothing so resistant as the dull security of possession: the stolidity of ownership!

Many times that day I stopped by a field side or at the end of a lane, or at a house-gate, and considered the possibilities of making an

attack.   Oh, I measured the houses and barns
I saw with a new eye!   The kind of country
I had known so long and familiarly became a
new and foreign land, full of strange possibilities.   I spied out the men in the fields and
did not fail, also, to see what I could of the
commissary department of each farmstead
as I passed.   I walked for miles looking thus
for a favourable opening — and with a sensation of embarrassment at once disagreeable
and pleasurable.   As the afternoon began to
deepen I saw that I must absolutely do something: a whole day tramping in the open air
without a bite to eat is an irresistible argument.

Presently I saw from the road a farmer and
his son planting potatoes in a sloping field.
There was no house at all in view.   At the
bars stood a light wagon half filled with bags
of seed potatoes, and the horse which had
drawn it stood quietly, not far off, tied to the
fence.   The man and the boy, each with a
basket on his arm, were at the farther end of
the field, dropping potatoes.   I stood quietly
watching them.   They stepped quickly and
kept their eyes on the furrows: good workers.
I liked the looks of them.   I liked also the

straight, clean furrows; I liked the appearance
of the horse.

"I will stop here," I said to myself.

I cannot at all convey the sense of high
adventure I had as I stood there. Though I
had not the slightest idea of what I should
do or say, yet I was determined upon the
attack.

Neither father nor son saw me until they
had nearly reached the end of the field.

"Step lively, Ben," I heard the man say
with some impatience; "we've got to finish
this field to-day."

"I *am* steppin' lively, dad," responded the
boy, "but it's awful hot. We can't possibly
finish to-day. It's too much."

"We've got to get through here to-day,"
the man replied grimly; "we're already two
weeks late."

I know just how the man felt; for I knew
well the difficulty a farmer has in getting help
in planting time. The spring waits for no
man. My heart went out to the man and boy
struggling there in the heat of their sloping
field. For this is the real warfare of the
common life.

"Why," I said to myself with a curious lift

"'I will stop here,' I said to myself"

of the heart, "they have need of a fellow just like me."

At that moment the boy saw me and, missing a step in the rhythm of the planting, the father also looked up and saw me. But neither said a word until the furrows were finished, and the planters came to refill their baskets.

"Fine afternoon," I said, sparring for an opening.

"Fine," responded the man rather shortly, glancing up from his work. I recalled the scores of times I had been exactly in his place, and had glanced up to see the stranger in the road.

"Got another basket handy?" I asked.

"There is one somewhere around here," he answered not too cordially. The boy said nothing at all, but eyed me with absorbing interest. The gloomy look had already gone from his face.

I slipped my gray bag from my shoulder, took off my coat, and put them both down inside the fence. Then I found the basket and began to fill it from one of the bags. Both man and boy looked up at me questioningly. I enjoyed the situation immensely.

"I heard you say to your son," I said, "that you'd have to hurry in order to get in your potatoes to-day. I can see that for myself. Let me take a hand for a row or two."

The unmistakable shrewd look of the bargainer came suddenly into the man's face, but when I went about my business without hesitation or questioning, he said nothing at all. As for the boy, the change in his countenance was marvellous to see. Something new and astonishing had come into the world. Oh, I know what a thing it is to be a boy and have to work in trouting time!

"How near are you planting, Ben?" I asked.

"About fourteen inches."

So we began in fine spirits. I was delighted with the favourable beginning of my enterprise; there is nothing which so draws men together as their employment at a common task.

Ben was a lad some fifteen years old — very stout and stocky, with a fine open countenance and a frank blue eye — all boy. His nose was as freckled as the belly of a trout. The whole situation, including the prospect of help in finishing a tiresome job, pleased him hugely. He stole a glimpse from time to time at me and then at his father. Finally he said:

"Say, you'll have to step lively to keep up with dad."

"I'll show you," I said, "how we used to drop potatoes when I was a boy."

And with that I began to step ahead more quickly and make the pieces fairly fly.

"We old fellows," I said to the father, "must give these young sprouts a lesson once in a while."

"You will, will you?" responded the boy, and instantly began to drop the potatoes at a prodigious speed. The father followed with more dignity, but with evident amusement, and so we all came with a rush to the end of the row.

"I guess that beats the record across *this* field!" remarked the lad, puffing and wiping his forehead. "Say, but you're a good one!"

It gave me a peculiar thrill of pleasure; there is nothing more pleasing than the frank admiration of a boy.

We paused a moment and I said to the man:

"This looks like fine potato land."

"The' ain't any better in these parts," he replied with some pride in his voice.

And so we went at the planting again: and as we planted we had great talk of seed potatoes and the advantages and disadvantages of mechanical planters, of cultivating and spraying, and all the lore of prices and profits. Once we stopped at the lower end of the field to get a drink from a jug of water set in the shade of a fence corner, and once we set the horse in the thills and moved the seed farther up the field. And tired and hungry as I felt I really enjoyed the work; I really enjoyed talking with this busy father and son, and I wondered what their home life was like and what were their real ambitions and hopes. Thus the sun sank lower and lower, the long shadows began to creep into the valleys, and we came finally toward the end of the field. Suddenly the boy Ben cried out:

"There's Sis!"

I glanced up and saw standing near the gateway a slim, bright girl of about twelve in a fresh gingham dress.

"We're coming!" roared Ben, exultantly.

While we were hitching up the horse, the man said to me:

"You'll come down with us and have some supper."

"Indeed I will," I replied, trying not to make my response too eager.

"Did mother make gingerbread to-day?" I heard the boy whisper audibly.

"Sh-h —" replied the girl; "who is that man?"

"*I* don't know" — with a great accent of mystery — "and dad don't know. Did mother make gingerbread?"

"Sh-h — he'll hear you."

"Gee! but he can plant potatoes. He dropped down on us out of a clear sky."

"What is he?" she asked. "A tramp?"

"Nope, not a tramp. He works. But, Sis, did mother make gingerbread?"

So we all got into the light wagon and drove briskly out along the shady country road. The evening was coming on, and the air was full of the scent of blossoms. We turned finally into a lane and thus came promptly, for the horse was as eager as we, to the capacious farmyard. A motherly woman came out from the house, spoke to her son, and nodded pleasantly to me. There was no especial introduction. I said merely, "My name is Grayson," and I was accepted without a word.

I waited to help the man, whose name I had now learned — it was Stanley — with his horse and wagon, and then we came up to the house. Near the back door there was a pump, with a bench and basin set just within a little cleanly swept, open shed. Rolling back my collar and baring my arms I washed myself in the cool water, dashing it over my head until I gasped, and then stepping back, breathless and refreshed, I found the slim girl, Mary, at my elbow with a clean soft towel. As I stood wiping quietly I could smell the ambrosial odours from the kitchen. In all my life I never enjoyed a moment more than that, I think.

"Come in now," said the motherly Mrs. Stanley.

So we filed into the roomy kitchen, where an older girl, called Kate, was flying about placing steaming dishes upon the table. There was also an older son, who had been at the farm chores. It was altogether a fine, vigorous, independent American family. So we all sat down and drew up our chairs. Then we paused a moment, and the father, bowing his head, said in a low voice:

"For all Thy good gifts, Lord, we thank Thee. Preserve us and keep us through another night."

I suppose it was a very ordinary farm meal, but it seems to me I never tasted a better one. The huge piles of new baked bread, the sweet farm butter, already delicious with the flavour of new grass, the bacon and eggs, the potatoes, the rhubarb sauce, the great plates of new, hot gingerbread and, at the last, the custard pie — a great wedge of it, with fresh cheese. After the first ravenous appetite of hardworking men was satisfied, there came to be a good deal of lively conversation. The girls had some joke between them which Ben was trying in vain to fathom. The older son told how much milk a certain Alderney cow had given, and Mr. Stanley, quite changed now as he sat at his own table from the rather grim farmer of the afternoon, revealed a capacity for a husky sort of fun, joking Ben about his potato-planting and telling in a lively way of his race with me. As for Mrs Stanley, she sat smiling behind her tall coffee pot, radiating good cheer and hospitality. They asked me no questions at all, and I was so hungry and tired that I volunteered no information.

After supper we went out for half or three quarters of an hour to do some final chores, and Mr. Stanley and I stopped in the cattle yard and looked over the cows, and talked learnedly about the pigs, and I admired his spring calves to his heart's content, for they really were a fine lot.   When we came in again the lamps had been lighted in the sitting-room and the older daughter was at the telephone exchanging the news of the day with some neighbour — and with great laughter and enjoyment. Occasionally she would turn and repeat some bit of gossip to the family, and Mrs. Stanley would exclaim:

"Do tell!"

"Can't we have a bit of music to-night?" inquired Mr. Stanley.

Instantly Ben and the slim girl, Mary, made a wild dive for the front room — the parlour — and came out with a firstrate phonograph which they placed on the table.

"Something lively now," said Mr. Stanley.

So they put on a rollicking negro song called "My Georgia Belle," which, besides the tuneful voices, introduced a steamboat whistle and a musical clangour of bells.   When it wound up with a bang, Mr. Stanley took his big comfortable pipe out of his mouth and cried out:

"Fine, fine!"

We had further music of the same sort and with one record the older daughter, Kate, broke into the song with a full, strong though uncultivated voice — which pleased us all very much indeed.

Presently Mrs. Stanley, who was sitting under the lamp with a basket of socks to mend, began to nod.

"Mother's giving the signal," said the older son.

"No, no, I'm not a bit sleepy," exclaimed Mrs. Stanley.

But with further joking and laughing the family began to move about. The older daughter gave me a hand lamp and showed me the way upstairs to a little room at the end of the house.

"I think," she said with pleasant dignity, "you will find everything you need."

I cannot tell with what solid pleasure I rolled into bed or how soundly and sweetly I slept.

This was the first day of my real adventures.

I WHISTLE

CHAPTER II

I WHISTLE

WHEN I was a boy I learned after many discouragements to play on a tin whistle. There was a wandering old fellow in our town who would sit for hours on the shady side of a certain ancient hotel-barn, and with his little whistle to his lips, and gently swaying his head to his tune and tapping one foot in the gravel, he would produce the most wonderful and beguiling melodies. His favourite selections were very lively; he played, I remember, "Old Dan Tucker," and "Money Musk," and the tune of a rollicking old song, now no doubt long forgotten, called "Wait for the Wagon." I can see him yet, with his jolly eyes half closed, his lips puckered around the whistle, and his fingers curiously and stiffly poised over the stops. I am sure I shall never forget the thrill which his music gave to the heart of a certain barefoot boy.

At length, by means I have long since forgotten, I secured a tin whistle exactly like Old Tom Madison's and began diligently to practise such tunes as I knew. I am quite sure now that I must have made a nuisance of myself, for it soon appeared to be the set purpose of every member of the family to break up my efforts. Whenever my father saw me with the whistle to my lips, he would instantly set me at some useful work (oh, he was an adept in discovering useful work to do — for a boy!). And at the very sight of my stern aunt I would instantly secrete my whistle in my blouse and fly for the garret or cellar, like a cat caught in the cream. Such are the early tribulations of musical genius!

At last I discovered a remote spot on a beam in the hay-barn where, lighted by a ray of sunlight which came through a crack in the eaves and pointed a dusty golden finger into that hay-scented interior, I practised rapturously and to my heart's content upon my tin whistle. I learned "Money Musk" until I could play it in Old Tom Madison's best style — even to the last nod and final foot-tap. I turned a certain church hymn called "Yield Not to Temptation" into something quite inspiriting, and I played "Marching Through Georgia" until all the "happy hills of hay" were to the fervid eye of a boy's imagination full of tramping soldiers. Oh, I shall never forget the joys of those hours in the hay-barn, nor the music of that secret tin whistle! I can hear yet the crooning of the pigeons in the eaves, and the slatey sound of their wings as they flew across the open spaces in the great barn; I can smell yet the odour of the hay.

But with years, and the city, and the shame of youth, I put aside and almost forgot the art of whistling. When I was preparing for the present pilgrimage, however, it came to me with a sudden thrill of pleasure that nothing in the wide world now prevented me from getting a whistle and seeing whether I had forgotten my early cunning At the very first good-sized town I came to I was delighted to find at a little candy and toy shop just the sort of whistle I wanted, at the extravagant price of ten cents. I bought it and put it in the bottom of my knapsack.

"Am I not old enough now," I said to myself, "to be as youthful as I choose?"

Isn't it the strangest thing in the world how long it takes us to learn to accept the joys of simple pleasures? — and some of us never learn at all. "Boo!" says the neighbourhood, and we are instantly frightened into doing a thousand unnecessary and unpleasant things, or prevented from doing a thousand beguiling things.

For the first few days I was on the road I thought often with pleasure of the whistle lying there in my bag, but it was not until after I left the Stanleys' that I felt exactly in the mood to try it.

The fact is, my adventures on the Stanley farm had left me in a very cheerful frame of mind. They convinced me that some of the great things I had expected of my pilgrimage were realizable possibilities. Why, I had walked right into the heart of as fine a family as I have seen these many days.

I remained with them the entire day following the patoto-planting. We were out at five o'clock in the morning, and after helping with the chores, and eating a prodigious breakfast, we went again to the potato-field, and part of the time I helped plant a few remaining rows, and part of the time I drove a team attached to a wing-plow to cover the planting of the previous day.

In the afternoon a slashing spring rain set in, and Mr. Stanley, who was a fore-handed worker, found a job for all of us in the barn. Ben, the younger son, and I sharpened mower-blades and a scythe or so, Ben turning the grindstone and I holding the blades and telling him stories into the bargain. Mr. Stanley and his stout older son overhauled the work-harness and tinkered the corn-planter. The doors at both ends of the barn stood wide open, and through one of them, framed like a picture, we could see the scudding floods descend upon the meadows, and through the other, across a fine stretch of open country, we could see all the roads glistening and the tree-tops moving under the rain.

"Fine, fine!" exclaimed Mr. Stanley, look-ing out from time to time, "we got in our potatoes just in the nick of time."

After supper that evening I told them of my plan to leave them on the following morning.

"Don't do that," said Mrs. Stanley heartily; "stay on with us."

"Yes," said Mr. Stanley, "we're shorthanded, and I'd be glad to have a man like you all summer. There ain't any one around here will pay a good man more'n I will, nor treat 'im better."

"I'm sure of it, Mr. Stanley," I said, "but I can't stay with you."

At that the tide of curiosity which I had seen rising ever since I came began to break through. Oh, I know how difficult it is to let the wanderer get by without taking toll of him! There are not so many people here in the country that we can afford to neglect them. And as I had nothing in the world to conceal, and, indeed, loved nothing better than the give and take of getting acquainted, we were soon at it in good earnest.

But it was not enough to tell them that my name was David Grayson and where my farm was located, and how many acres there were, and how much stock I had, and what I raised. The great particular "Why?" — as I knew it would be — concerned my strange presence on the road at this season of the year and the reason why I should turn in by chance, as I had done, to help at their planting. If a man is stationary, it seems quite impossible for him to imagine why any one should care to wander; and as for the wanderer it is inconceivable to him how any one can remain permanently at home.

We were all sitting comfortably around the table in the living-room. The lamps were lighted, and Mr. Stanley, in slippers, was smoking his pipe and Mrs. Stanley was darning socks over a mending-gourd, and the two young Stanleys were whispering and giggling about some matter of supreme consequence to youth. The windows were open, and we could smell the sweet scent of the lilacs from the yard and hear the drumming of the rain as it fell on the roof of the porch.

"It's easy to explain," I said. "The fact is, it got to the point on my farm that I wasn't quite sure whether I owned it or it owned me. And I made up my mind I'd get away for a while from my own horses and cattle and see what the world was like. I wanted to see how people lived up here, and what they are thinking about, and how they do their farming."

As I talked of my plans and of the duty one had, as I saw it, to be a good broad man as well as a good farmer, I grew more and more interested and enthusiastic. Mr. Stanley took his pipe slowly from his mouth, held it poised until it finally went out, and sat looking at me with a rapt expression. I never had a better audience. Finally, Mr. Stanley said very earnestly:

"And you have felt that way, too?"

"Why, father!" exclaimed Mrs. Stanley, in astonishment.

Mr. Stanley hastily put his pipe back into his mouth and confusedly searched in his pockets for a match; but I knew I had struck down deep into a common experience. Here was this brisk and prosperous farmer having his dreams too — dreams that even his wife did not know!

So I continued my talk with even greater fervour. I don't think that the boy Ben understood all that I said, for I was dealing with experiences common mostly to older men, but he somehow seemed to get the spirit of it, for quite unconsciously he began to hitch his chair toward me, then he laid his hand on my chair-arm and finally and quite simply he rested his arm against mine and looked at me with all his eyes. I keep learning that there is nothing which reaches men's hearts like talking straight out the convictions and emotions of your innermost soul. Those who hear you may not agree with you, or they may not understand you fully, but something incalculable, something vital, passes. And as for a boy or girl it is one of the sorriest of mistakes to talk down to them; almost always your lad of fifteen thinks more simply, more fundamentally, than you do; and what he accepts as good coin is not facts or precepts, but feelings and convictions — *life*. And why shouldn't we speak out?

"I long ago decided," I said, "to try to be fully what I am and not to be anything or anybody else."

"That's right, that's right!" exclaimed Mr. Stanley, nodding his head vigorously.

"It's about the oldest wisdom there is," I said, and with that I thought of the volume I carried in my pocket, and straightway I pulled it out and after a moment's search found the passage I wanted.

"Listen," I said, "to what this old Roman philosopher said" — and I held the book up to the lamp and read aloud:

"'You can be invincible if you enter into no contest in which it is not in your power to conquer. Take care, then, when you observe a man honoured before others or possessed of great power, or highly esteemed for any reason, not to suppose him happy and be not carried away by the appearance. For if the nature of the good is in our power, neither envy nor jealousy will have a place in us. But you yourself will not wish to be a general or a senator or consul, but a free man, and there is only one way to do this, to care not for the things which are not in our power."

"That," said Mr. Stanley triumphantly, "is exactly what I've always said, but I didn't know it was in any book. I always said I didn't want to be a senator or a legislator, or any other sort of office-holder. It's good enough for me right here on this farm."

At that moment I glanced down into Ben's shining eyes.

"But I want to be a senator or — something — when I grow up," he said eagerly.

At this the older brother, who was sitting not far off, broke into a laugh, and the boy, who for a moment had been drawn out of his reserve, shrank back again and coloured to the hair.

"Well, Ben," said I, putting my hand on his knee, "don't you let anything stop you. I'll back you up; I'll vote for you."

After breakfast the next morning Mr. Stanley drew me aside and said:

"Now I want to pay you for your help yesterday and the day before."

"No," I said. "I've had more than value received. You've taken me in like a friend and brother. I've enjoyed it."

So Mrs. Stanley half filled my knapsack with the finest luncheon I've seen in many a day, and thus, with as pleasant a farewell as if I'd been a near relative, I set off up the country road. I was a little distressed in parting to see nothing of the boy Ben, for I had formed a genuine liking for him, but upon reaching a clump of trees which hid the house from the road I saw him standing in the moist grass of a fence corner.

"I want to say good-bye," he said in the gruff voice of embarrassment.

"Ben," I said, "I missed you, and I'd have hated to go off without seeing you again. Walk a bit with me."

So we walked side by side, talking quietly, and when at last I shook his hand I said:

"Ben, don't you ever be afraid of acting up to the very best thoughts you have in your heart."

He said nothing for a moment, and then: "Gee! I'm sorry you're goin' away!"

"Gee!" I responded, "I'm sorry, too!"

With that we both laughed, but when I reached the top of the hill, and looked back, I saw him still standing there barefooted in the road looking after me. I waved my hand and he waved his: and I saw him no more.

No country, after all, produces any better crop than its inhabitants. And as I travelled onward I liked to think of these brave, temperate, industrious, God-friendly American people. I have no fear of the country while so many of them are still to be found upon the farms and in the towns of this land.

So I tramped onward full of cheerfulness.

The rain had ceased, but all the world was moist and very green and still. I walked for more than two hours with the greatest pleasure. About ten o'clock in the morning I stopped near a brook to drink and rest, for I was warm and tired. And it was then that I bethought me of the little tin pipe in my knapsack, and straightway I got it out, and, sitting down at the foot of a tree near the brook, I put it to my lips and felt for the stops with unaccustomed fingers. At first I made the saddest sort of work of it, and was not a little disappointed, indeed, with the sound of the whistle itself. It was nothing to my memory of it! It seemed thin and tinny.

However, I persevered at it, and soon produced a recognizable imitation of Tom Madison's "Old Dan Tucker." My success quite pleased me, and I became so absorbed that I quite lost account of the time and place. There was no one to hear me save a bluejay which for an hour or more kept me company. He sat on a twig just across the brook, cocking his head at me, and saucily wagging his tail. Occasionally he would dart away among the trees crying shrilly; but his curiosity would always get the better of him and back he would come again to try to solve the mystery of this rival whistling, which I'm sure was as shrill and as harsh as his own.

Presently, quite to my astonishment, I saw a man standing near the brookside not a dozen paces away from me. How long he had been there I don't know, for I had heard nothing of his coming. Beyond him in the town road I could see the head of his horse and the top of his buggy. I said not a word, but continued with my practising. Why shouldn't I? But it gave me quite a thrill for the moment; and at once I began to think of the possibilities of the situation. What a thing it was to have so many unexpected and interesting situations developing! So I nodded my head and tapped my foot, and blew into my whistle all the more energetically. I knew my visitor could not possibly keep away. And he could not; presently he came nearer and said:

"What are you doing, neighbour?"

I continued a moment with my playing, but commanded him with my eye.

"WHAT ARE YOU DOING, NEIGHBOUR?"

Oh, I assure you I assumed all the airs of a virtuoso. When I had finished my tune I removed my whistle deliberately and wiped my lips.

"Why, enjoying myself," I replied with greatest good humour. "What are you doing?"

"Why," he said, "watching you enjoy yourself. I heard you playing as I passed in the road, and couldn't imagine what it could be."

I told him I thought it might still be difficult, having heard me near at hand, to imagine what it could be — and thus, tossing the ball of good-humoured repartee back and forth, we walked down to the road together. He had a quiet old horse and a curious top buggy with the unmistakable box of an agent or peddler built on behind.

"My name," he said, "is Canfield. I fight dust."

"And mine," I said, "is Grayson. I whistle."

I discovered that he was an agent for brushes, and he opened his box and showed me the greatest assortment of big and little brushes: bristle brushes, broom brushes, yarn brushes, wire brushes, brushes for man and brushes for beast, brushes of every conceivable size and shape that ever I saw in all my life. He had out one of his especial pets — he called it his "leader" — and feeling it familiarly in his hand he instinctively began the jargon of well-handled and voice-worn phrases which went with that particular brush. It was just as though some one had touched a button and had started him going. It was amazing to me that any one in the world should be so much interested in mere brushes — until he actually began to make me feel that brushes were as interesting as anything else!

What a strange, little, dried-up old fellow he was, with his balls of muttonchop side-whiskers, his thick eyebrows, and his lively blue eyes! — a man evidently not readily turned aside by rebuffs. He had already shown that his wit as a talker had been sharpened by long and varied contact with a world of reluctant purchasers. I was really curious to know more of him, so I said finally:

"See here, Mr. Canfield, it's just noon. Why not sit down here with me and have a bit of luncheon?"

"Why not?" he responded with alacrity. "As the fellow said, why not?"

He unhitched his horse, gave him a drink from the brook, and then tethered him where he could nip the roadside grass. I opened my bag and explored the wonders of Mrs. Stanley's luncheon. I cannot describe the absolutely carefree feeling I had. Always at home, when I would have liked to stop at the roadside with a stranger, I felt the nudge of a conscience troubled with cows and corn, but here I could stop where I liked, or go on when I liked, and talk with whom I pleased, as long as I pleased.

So we sat there, the brush-peddler and I, under the trees, and ate Mrs. Stanley's fine luncheon, drank the clear water from the brook, and talked great talk. Compared with Mr. Canfield I was a babe at wandering — and equally at talking. Was there any business he had not been in, or any place in the country he had not visited? He had sold everything from fly-paper to threshing-machines, he had picked up a large working knowledge of the weaknesses of human nature, and had arrived at the age of sixty-six with just enough available cash to pay the manufacturer for a new supply of brushes. In strict confidence, I drew certain conclusions from the colour of his nose! He had once had a family, but dropped them somewhere along the road. Most of our brisk neighbours would have put him down as a failure — an old man, and nothing laid by! But I wonder — I wonder —— One thing I am coming to learn in this world, and that is to let people haggle along with their lives as I haggle along with mine.

We both made tremendous inroads on the luncheon, and I presume we might have sat there talking all the afternoon if I had not suddenly bethought myself with a not unpleasant thrill that my resting-place for the night was still gloriously un-decided.

"Friend," I said, "I've got to be up and going. I haven't so much as a penny in my pocket, and I've got to find a place to sleep."

The effect of this remark upon Mr. Can-field was magical. He threw up both hands and cried out:

"You're that way, are you?" — as though

for the first time he really understood. We were at last on common ground.

"Partner," said he, "you needn't tell me nothin' about it. I've been right there myself."

At once he began to bustle about with great enthusiasm. He was for taking complete charge of me, and I think, if I had permitted it, would instantly have made a brush-agent of me. At least he would have carried me along with him in his buggy; but when he suggested it I felt very much, I think, as some old monk must have felt who had taken a vow to do some particular thing in some particular way. With great difficulty I convinced him finally that my way was different from his — though he was regally impartial as to what road he took next — and, finally, with some reluctance, he started to climb into his buggy.

A thought, however, struck him suddenly, and he stepped down again, ran around to the box at the back of his buggy, opened it with a mysterious and smiling look at me, and took out a small broom-brush with which he instantly began brushing off my coat and trousers — in the liveliest and most exuberant way. When he had finished this occupation, he quickly handed the brush to me.

"A token of esteem," he said, "from a fellow traveller."

I tried in vain to thank him, but he held up his hand, scrambled quickly into his buggy, and was for driving off instantly, but paused and beckoned me toward him. When I approached the buggy, he took hold of one the lapels of my coat, bent over, and said with the utmost seriousness:

"No man ought to take the road without a brush. A good broom-brush is the world's greatest civilizer. Are you looking seedy or dusty? — why, this here brush will instantly make you a respectable citizen. Take my word for it, friend, never go into any strange house without stoppin' and brushin' off. It's money in your purse! You can get along without dinner sometimes, or even without a shirt, but without a brush — never! There's nothin' in the world so necessary to rich *an'* poor, old *an'* young as a good brush!"

And with a final burst of enthusiasm the brush-peddler drove off up the hill.

I stood watching him and when he looked around I waved the brush high over my head in token of a grateful farewell.

It was a good, serviceable, friendly brush. I carried it throughout my wanderings; and as I sit here writing in my study, at this moment, I can see it hanging on a hook at the side of my fireplace.

THE HOUSE BY THE SIDE
OF THE ROAD

CHAPTER III

THE HOUSE BY THE SIDE OF THE ROAD

EVERY one," remarks Tristram Shandy, "will speak of the fair as his own market has gone in it."

It came near being a sorry fair for me on the afternoon following my parting with the amiable brush-peddler. The plain fact is, my success at the Stanleys', and the easy manner in which I had fallen in with Mr. Canfield, gave me so much confidence in myself as a sort of Master of the Road that I proceeded with altogether too much assurance.

I am firmly convinced that the prime quality to be cultivated by the pilgrim is humility of spirit; he must be willing to accept Adventure in whatever garb she chooses to present herself. He must be able to see the shining form of the unusual through the dull garments of the normal.

The fact is, I walked that afternoon with my head in air and passed many a pleasant farmstead where men were working in the fields, and many an open doorway, and a mill or two, and a town — always looking for some Great Adventure.

Somewhere upon this road, I thought to myself, I shall fall in with a Great Person, or become a part of a Great Incident. I recalled with keen pleasure the experience of that young Spanish student of whom Carlyle writes in one of his volumes, who, riding out from Madrid one day, came unexpectedly upon the greatest man in the world. This great man, of whom Carlyle observes (I have looked up the passage since I came home), "a kindlier, meeker, or braver heart has seldom looked upon the sky in this world," had ridden out from the city for the last time in his life "to

take one other look at the azure firmament
and green mosaic pavements and the strange
carpentry and arras work of this noble palace of a world."

As the old story has it, the young student
"came pricking on hastily, complaining that
they went at such a pace as gave him little
chance of keeping up with them. One of
the party made answer that the blame lay
with the horse of Don Miguel de Cervantes,
whose trot was of the speediest. He had
hardly pronounced the name when the student dismounted and, touching the hem of
Cervantes' left sleeve, said, 'Yes, yes, it is
indeed the maimed perfection, the all-famous,
the delightful writer, the joy and darling of
the Muses! You are that brave Miguel.'"

It may seem absurd to some in this cool
and calculating twentieth century that any
one should indulge in such vain imaginings
as I have described — and yet, why not?
All things are as we see them. I once heard
a man — a modern man, living to-day —
tell with a hush in his voice, and a peculiar
light in his eye, how, walking in the outskirts
of an unromantic town in New Jersey, he
came suddenly upon a vigorous, bearded,

rather rough-looking man swinging his stick as he walked, and stopping often at the roadside and often looking up at the sky. I shall never forget the curious thrill in his voice as he said:

"And *that* was Walt Whitman."

And thus quite absurdly intoxicated by the possibilities of the road, I let the big, full afternoon slip by — I let slip the rich possibilities of half a hundred farms and scores of travelling people — and as evening began to fall I came to a stretch of wilder country with wooded hills and a dashing stream by the roadside. It was a fine and beautiful country — to look at — but the farms, and with them the chances of dinner, and a friendly place to sleep, grew momentarily scarcer. Upon the hills here and there, indeed, were to be seen the pretentious summer homes of rich dwellers from the cities, but I looked upon them with no great hopefulness.

"Of all places in the world," I said to myself, "surely none could be more unfriendly to a man like me."

But I amused myself with conjectures as to what might happen (until the adventure seemed almost worth trying) if a dusty man with a bag on his back should appear at the door of one of those well-groomed establishments. It came to me, indeed, with a sudden deep sense of understanding, that I should probably find there, as everywhere else, just men and women. And with that I fell into a sort of Socratic dialogue with myself:

ME: Having decided that the people in these houses are, after all, merely men and women, what is the best way of reaching them?

MYSELF: Undoubtedly by giving them something they want and have not.

ME: But these are rich people from the city; what can they want that they have not?

MYSELF: Believe me, of all people in the world those who want the most are those who have the most. These people are also consumed with desires.

ME: And what, pray, do you suppose they desire?

MYSELF: They want what they have not got; they want the unattainable: they want chiefly the rarest and most precious of all things — a little mystery in their lives.

"That's it!" I said aloud; "that's it!

Mystery — the things of the spirit, the things above ordinary living—is not that the essential thing for which the world is sighing, and groaning, and longing — consciously, or unconsciously?"

I have always believed that men in their innermost souls desire the highest, bravest, finest things they can hear, or see, or feel in all the world. Tell a man how he can increase his income and he will be grateful to you and soon forget you; but show him the highest, most mysterious things in his own soul and give him the word which will convince him that the finest things are really attainable, and he will love and follow you always.

I now began to look with much excitement to a visit at one of the houses on the hill, but to my disappointment I found the next two that I approached still closed up, for the spring was not yet far enough advanced to attract the owners to the country. I walked rapidly onward through the gathering twilight, but with increasing uneasiness as to the prospects for the night, and thus came suddenly upon the scene of an odd adventure.

From some distance I had seen a veritable palace set high among the trees and overlooking a wonderful green valley — and, drawing nearer, I saw evidences of well-kept roadways and a visible effort to make invisible the attempt to preserve the wild beauty of the place. I saw, or thought I saw, people on the wide veranda, and I was sure I heard the snort of a climbing motor-car, but I had scarcely decided to make my way up to the house when I came, at the turning of the country road, upon a bit of open land laid out neatly as a garden, near the edge of which, nestling among the trees, stood a small cottage. It seemed somehow to belong to the great estate above it, and I concluded, at the first glance, that it was the home of some caretaker or gardener.

It was a charming place to see, and especially the plantation of trees and shrubs. My eye fell instantly upon a fine magnolia — rare in this country — which had not yet cast all its blossoms, and I paused for a moment to look at it more closely. I myself have tried to raise magnolias near my house, and I know how difficult it is.

As I approached nearer to the cottage I could see a man and woman sitting upon the porch in the twilight and swaying back and forth in rocking-chairs. I fancied — it may have been only a fancy — that when I first saw them their hands were clasped as they rocked side by side.

It was indeed a charming little cottage. Crimson ramblers, giving promise of the bloom that was yet to come, climbed over one end of the porch, and there were fine dark-leaved lilac-bushes near the doorway: oh, a pleasant, friendly, quiet place!

I opened the front gate and walked straight in, as though I had at last reached my destination. I cannot give any idea of the lift of the heart with which I entered upon this new adventure. Without the slightest premeditation and not knowing what I should say or do, I realized that everything depended upon a few sentences spoken within the next minute or two. Believe me, this experience, to a man who does not know where his next meal is coming from, nor where he is to spend the night, is well worth having. It is a marvellous sharpener of the faculties.

I knew, of course, just how these quiet

people of the cottage would ordinarily regard an intruder whose bag and clothing must infallibly class him as a follower of the road. And so many followers of the road are — well ——

As I came nearer, the man and woman stopped rocking, but said nothing. An old dog that had been sleeping on the top step rose slowly and stood there.

"As I passed your garden," I said, grasping desperately for a way of approach, "I saw your beautiful specimen of the magnolia tree — the one still in blossom. I myself have tried to grow magnolias — but with small success — and I'm making bold to inquire what variety you are so successful with."

It was a shot in the air — but I knew from what I had seen that they must be enthusiastic gardeners. The man glanced around at the magnolia with evident pride, and was about to answer when the woman rose and with a pleasant, quiet cordiality said:

"Won't you step up and have a chair?"

I swung my bag from my shoulder and took the proffered seat. As I did so I saw, on the table just behind me a number of magazines and books — books of unusual sizes and shapes, indicating that they were not mere summer novels.

"They like books!" I said to myself with a sudden rise of spirits.

"I have tried magnolias, too," said the man, "but this is the only one that has been really successful. It is a Chinese white magnolia."

"The one Downing describes?" I asked.

This was also a random shot, but I conjectured that if they loved both books and gardens they would know Downing — the Bible of the gardener. And if they did, why, we belonged to the same church.

"The very same," exclaimed the woman; "it was Downing's enthusiasm for the Chinese magnolia which led us first to try it."

With that, like true disciples, we fell into great talk of Downing, at first all in praise of him, and later — for may not the faithful be permitted latitude in their comments so long as it is all within the cloister? — we indulged in a bit of higher criticism.

"It won't do," said the man, "to follow

too slavishly every detail of practice as rec-
ommended by Downing.   We have learned
a good many things since the forties."

"The fact is," I said, "no literal-minded
man should be trusted with Downing."

"Any more than with the Holy Scrip-
tures," exclaimed the woman.

"Exactly!" I responded with the greatest
enthusiasm; "exactly!   We go to him for
inspiration, for fundamental teachings, for
the great literature and poetry of the art.
Do you remember," I asked, "that passage
in which Downing quotes from some old
Chinaman upon the true secret of the pleasures of a garden —— ?"

"Do we?" exclaimed the man, jumping
up instantly; "do we?   Just let me get the
book ——"

With that he went into the house and
came back immediately bringing a lamp in
one hand — for it had grown pretty dark —
and a familiar, portly, blue-bound book in
the other.   While he was gone the woman
said:

"You have touched Mr. Vedder in his
weakest spot."

"I know of no combination in this world,"

said I, "so certain to produce a happy heart as good books and a farm or garden."

Mr. Vedder, having returned, slipped on his spectacles, sat forward on the edge of his rocking-chair, and opened the book with pious hands.

"I'll find it," he said. "I can put my finger right on it."

"You'll find it," said Mrs. Vedder, "in the chapter on 'Hedges.'"

"You are wrong, my dear," he responded, "it is in 'Mistakes of Citizens in Country Life.'"

He turned the leaves eagerly.

"No," he said, "here it is in 'Rural Taste.' Let me read you the passage, Mr. ——"

"Grayson."

"— Mr. Grayson. The Chinaman's name was Lieu-tscheu. 'What is it,' asks this old Chinaman, 'that we seek in the pleasure of a garden? It has always been agreed that these plantations should make men amends for living at a distance from what would be their more congenial and agreeable dwelling-place — in the midst of nature, free and unrestrained.'"

"That's it," I exclaimed, "and the old

Chinaman was right! A garden excuses civilization."

"It's what brought us here," said Mrs. Vedder.

With that we fell into the liveliest discussion of gardening and farming and country life in all their phases, resolving that while there were bugs and blights, and droughts and floods, yet upon the whole there was no life so completely satisfying as life in which one may watch daily the unfolding of natural life.

A hundred things we talked about freely that had often risen dimly in my own mind almost to the point — but not quite — of spilling over into articulate form. The marvellous thing about good conversation is that it brings to birth so many half-realized thoughts of our own — besides sowing the seed of innumerable other thought-plants. How they enjoyed their garden, those two, and not only the garden itself, but all the lore and poetry of gardening!

We had been talking thus an hour or more when, quite unexpectedly, I had what was certainly one of the most amusing adventures of my whole life. I can scarcely think of it now without a thrill of pleasure. I have had pay for my work in many ways, but never such a reward as this.

"By the way," said Mr. Vedder, "we have recently come across a book which is full of the spirit of the garden as we have long known it, although the author is not treating directly of gardens, but of farming and of human nature."

"It is really all one subject," I interrupted.

"Certainly," said Mr. Vedder, "but many gardeners are nothing but gardeners. Well, the book to which I refer is called 'Adventures in Contentment,' and is by —— Why, by a man of your own name!"

With that Mr. Vedder reached for a book — a familiar-looking book — on the table, but Mrs. Vedder looked at me. I give you my word, my heart turned entirely over, and in a most remarkable way righted itself again; and I saw Roman candles and Fourth of July rockets in front of my eyes. Never in all my experience was I so completely bowled over. I felt like a small boy who has been caught in the pantry with one hand in the jam-pot — and plenty of jam on his nose. And like that small boy I enjoyed the jam, but did not like being caught at it.

Mr. Vedder had no sooner got the book in his hand than I saw Mrs. Vedder rising as though she had seen a spectre, and pointing dramatically at me, she exclaimed:

"You are David Grayson!"

I can say truthfully now that I know how the prisoner at the bar must feel when the judge, leaning over his desk, looks at him sternly and says:

"I declare you guilty of the offence as charged, and sentence you ——" and so on, and so on.

Mr. Vedder stiffened up, and I can see him yet looking at me through his glasses. I must have looked as foolishly guilty as any man ever looked, for Mr. Vedder said promptly:

"Let me take you by the hand, sir. We know you, and have known you for a long time."

I shall not attempt to relate the conversation which followed, nor tell of the keen joy I had in it — after the first cold plunge. We found that we had a thousand common interests and enthusiasms. I had to tell them of my farm, and why I had left it temporarily, and of the experiences on the road. No sooner had I related what had befallen me at the Stanleys' than Mrs. Vedder disappeared into the house and came out again presently with a tray loaded with cold meat, bread, a pitcher of fine milk, and other good things.

"I shall not offer any excuses," said I, "I'm hungry," and with that I laid in, Mr. Vedder helping with the milk, and all three of us talking as fast as ever we could.

It was nearly midnight when at last Mr. Vedder led the way to the immaculate little bedroom where I spent the night.

The next morning I awoke early and, quietly dressing, slipped down to the garden and walked about among the trees and the shrubs and the flower-beds. The sun was just coming up over the hill, the air was full of the fresh odours of morning, and the orioles and cat-birds were singing.

In the back of the garden I found a charming rustic arbour with seats around a little table. And here I sat down to listen to the morning concert, and I saw, cut or carved upon the table, this verse, which so pleased me that I copied it in my book:

A garden is a lovesome thing, God wot!
    Rose plot,
    Fringed pool,
    Ferned grot —
The veriest school of peace; and yet
     the fool
    Contends that God is not —
Not God! in gardens? when the even
     is cool?
    Nay, but I have a sign,
'Tis very sure God walks in mine.

I looked about after copying this verse, and said aloud:

"I like this garden: I like these Vedders."

And with that I had a moment of wild enthusiasm.

"I will come," I said, "and buy a little garden next them, and bring Harriet, and we will live here always. What's a farm compared with a friend?"

But with that I thought of the Scotch preacher, and of Horace, and Mr. and Mrs. Starkweather, and I knew I could never leave the friends at home.

"It's astonishing how many fine people

there are in this world," I said aloud; "one can't escape them!"

"Good morning, David Grayson," I heard some one saying, and glancing up I saw Mrs. Vedder at the doorway. "Are you hungry?"

"I am always hungry," I said.

Mr. Vedder came out and linking his arm in mine and pointing out various spireas and Japanese barberries, of which he was very proud, we walked into the house together.

I did not think of it especially at the time — Harriet says I never see anything really worth while, by which she means dishes, dresses, doilies, and such like — but as I remembered afterward the table that Mrs. Vedder set was wonderfully dainty — dainty not merely with flowers (with which it was loaded), but with the quality of the china and silver. It was plainly the table of no ordinary gardener or caretaker — but this conclusion did not come to me until afterward, for as I remember it, we were in a deep discussion of fertilizers.

Mrs. Vedder cooked and served breakfast herself, and did it with a skill almost equal to Harriet's — so skilfully that the talk went

"GLANCING UP, I SAW MRS. VEDDER AT THE DOORWAY"

on and we never once heard the machinery of service.

After breakfast we all went out into the garden, Mrs. Vedder in an old straw hat and a big apron, and Mr. Vedder in a pair of old brown overalls. Two men had appeared from somewhere, and were digging in the vegetable garden. After giving them certain directions Mr. Vedder and I both found five-tined forks and went into the rose garden and began turning over the rich soil, while Mrs. Vedder, with pruning-shears, kept near us, cutting out the dead wood.

It was one of the charming forenoons of my life. This pleasant work, spiced with the most interesting conversation and interrupted by a hundred little excursions into other parts of the garden, to see this or that wonder of vegetation, brought us to dinner-time before we fairly knew it.

About the middle of the afternoon I made the next discovery. I heard first the choking cough of a big motor-car in the country road, and a moment later it stopped at our gate. I thought I saw the Vedders exchanging significant glances. A number of merry young people tumbled out, and an especially pretty girl of about twenty came running through the garden.

"Mother," she exclaimed, "you *must* come with us!"

"I can't, I can't," said Mrs. Vedder, "the roses *must* be pruned — and see! The azaleas are coming into bloom."

With that she presented me to her daughter.

And, then, shortly, for it could no longer be concealed, I learned that Mr. and Mrs. Vedder were not the caretakers but the owners of the estate and of the great house I had seen on the hill. That evening, with an air almost of apology, they explained to me how it all came about.

"We first came out here," said Mrs. Vedder, "nearly twenty years ago, and built the big house on the hill. But the more we came to know of country life the more we wanted to get down into it. We found it impossible up there — so many unnecessary things to see to and care for — and we couldn't — we didn't see ——"

"The fact is," Mr. Vedder put in, "we were losing touch with each other."

"There is nothing like a big house," said Mrs. Vedder, "to separate a man and his wife."

"So we came down here," said Mr. Vedder, "built this little cottage, and have developed this garden mostly with our own hands. We would have sold the big place long ago if it hadn't been for our friends. They like it."

"I have never heard a more truly romantic story," said I.

And it *was* romantic: these fine people escaping from too many possessions, too much property, to the peace and quietude of a garden where they could be lovers again.

"It seems, sometimes," said Mrs. Vedder, "that I never really believed in God until we came down here ——"

"I saw the verse on the table in your arbour," said I.

"And it is true," said Mr. Vedder. "We got a long, long way from God for many years: here we seem to get back to Him."

I had fully intended to take the road again that afternoon, but how could any one leave such people as those? We talked again late that night, but the next morning, at the leisurely Sunday breakfast, I set my hour of departure with all the firmness I could command. I left them, indeed, before ten o'clock that forenoon. I shall never forget the parting. They walked with me to the top of the hill, and there we stopped and looked back. We could see the cottage half hidden among the trees, and the little opening that the precious garden made. For a time we stood there quite silent.

"Do you remember," I said presently, "that character in Homer who was a friend of men and lived in a house by the side of the road? I shall always think of you as friends of men — you took in a dusty traveller. And I shall never forget your house by the side of the road."

"The House by the Side of the Road — you have christened it anew, David Grayson," exclaimed Mrs. Vedder.

And so we parted like old friends, and I left them to return to their garden, where " 'tis very sure God walks."

I AM A SPECTATOR OF A MIGHTY BATTLE, IN WHICH CHRISTIAN AGAIN MEETS APOLLYON

CHAPTER IV

I AM A SPECTATOR OF A MIGHTY BATTLE, IN WHICH CHRISTIAN AGAIN MEETS APOLLYON

IT IS one of the prime joys of the long road that no two days are ever remotely alike — no two hours even; and sometimes a day that begins calmly will end with the most stirring events.

It was thus, indeed, with that perfect spring Sunday when I left my friends, the Vedders, and turned my face again to the open country. It began as quietly as any Sabbath morning of my life, but what an end it had! I would have travelled a thou-

sand miles for the adventures which a bounteous road that day spilled carelessly into
my willing hands.

I can give no adequate reason why it
should be so, but there are Sunday mornings
in the spring — at least in our country —
which seem to put on, like a Sabbath gar-
ment, an atmosphere of divine quietude.
Warm, soft, clear, but, above all, immeasurably serene.

Such was that Sunday morning; and I
was no sooner well afoot than I yielded to
the ingratiating mood of the day. Usually
I am an active walker, loving the sense of
quick motion and the stir it imparts to
both body and mind, but that morning I
found myself loitering, looking widely about
me, and enjoying the lesser and quieter
aspects of nature. It was a fine wooded
country in which I found myself, and I soon
struck off the beaten road and took to the
forest and the fields. In places the ground
was almost covered with meadow-rue, like
green shadows on the hillsides, not yet in
seed, but richly umbrageous. In the long
green grass of the meadows shone the yellow
star-flowers, and the sweet-flags were bloom-

ing along the marshy edges of the ponds.
The violets had disappeared, but they were
succeeded by wild geraniums and rank-grow-
ing vetches.

I remember that I kept thinking from
time to time, all the forenoon, as my mind
went back swiftly and warmly to the two
fine friends from whom I had so recently
parted:

How the Vedders would enjoy this! Or,
I must tell the Vedders that. And two or
three times I found myself in animated con-
versations with them in which I generously
supplied all three parts. It may be true
for some natures, as Leonardo said, that
"if you are alone you belong wholly to yourself; if you have a companion, you belong
only half to yourself"; but it is certainly
not so with me. With me friendship never
divides: it multiplies. A friend always makes
me more than I am, better than I am, bigger
than I am. We two make four, or fifteen,
or forty.

Well, I loitered through the fields and
woods for a long time that Sunday forenoon,
not knowing in the least that Chance held
me close by the hand and was leading me

onward to great events. I knew, of course, that I had yet to find a place for the night, and that this might be difficult on Sunday, and yet I spent that forenoon as a man spends his immortal youth — with a glorious disregard for the future.

Some time after noon — for the sun was high and the day was growing much warmer — I turned from the road, climbed an inviting little hill, and chose a spot in an old meadow in the shade of an apple tree, and there I lay down on the grass and looked up into the dusky shadows of the branches above me. I could feel the soft airs on my face; I could hear the buzzing of bees in the meadow flowers, and by turning my head just a little I could see the slow fleecy clouds, high up, drifting across the perfect blue of the sky. And the scent of the fields in spring! — he who has known it, even once, may indeed die happy.

Men worship God in various ways: it seemed to me that Sabbath morning, as I lay quietly there in the warm silence of midday, that I was truly worshipping God. That Sunday morning everything about me seemed somehow to be a miracle — a miracle gratefully accepted and explainable only by the presence of God. There was another strange, deep feeling which I had that morning, which I have had a few other times in my life at the rare heights of experience — I hesitate always when I try to put down the deep, deep things of the human heart — a feeling immeasurably real, that if I should turn my head quickly I should indeed *see* that Immanent Presence. . . .

One of the few birds I know that sings through the long midday is the vireo. The vireo sings when otherwise the woods are still. You do not see him; you cannot find him; but you know he is there. And his singing is wild, and shy, and mystical. Often it haunts you like the memory of some former happiness. That day I heard the vireo singing. . . .

I don't know how long I lay there under the tree in the meadow, but presently I heard, from no great distance, the sound of a church-bell. It was ringing for the afternoon service which among the farmers of this part of the country often takes the place, in summer, of both morning and evening services.

"I believe I'll go," I said, thinking first of all, I confess, of the interesting people I might meet there.

But when I sat up and looked about me the desire faded, and rummaging in my bag I came across my tin whistle. Immediately I began practising a tune called "Sweet Afton," which I had learned when a boy; and, as I played, my mood changed swiftly, and I began to smile at myself as a tragically serious person, and to think of pat phrases with which to characterize the execrableness of my attempts upon the tin whistle. I should have liked some one near to joke with.

Long ago I made a motto about boys: Look for a boy anywhere. Never be surprised when you shake a cherry tree if a boy drops out of it; never be disturbed when you think yourself in complete solitude if you discover a boy peering out at you from a fence corner.

I had not been playing long before I saw two boys looking at me from out of a thicket by the roadside; and a moment later two others appeared.

Instantly I switched into "Marching

Through Georgia," and began to nod my head and tap my toe in the liveliest fashion. Presently one boy climbed up on the fence, then another, then a third. I continued to play. The fourth boy, a little chap, ventured to climb up on the fence.

They were bright-faced, tow-headed lads, all in Sunday clothes.

"It's hard luck," said I, taking my whistle from my lips, "to have to wear shoes and stockings on a warm Sunday like this."

"You bet it is!" said the bold leader.

"In that case," said I, "I will play 'Yankee Doodle.'"

I played. All the boys, including the little chap, came up around me, and two of them sat down quite familiarly on the grass. I never had a more devoted audience. I don't know what interesting event might have happened next, for the bold leader, who stood nearest, was becoming dangerously inflated with questions — I don't know what might have happened had we not been interrupted by the appearance of a Spectre in Black. It appeared before us there in the broad daylight in the middle of a sunny afternoon while we were playing "Yankee

Doodle." First I saw the top of a black hat rising over the rim of the hill. This was followed quickly by a black tie, a long black coat, black trousers, and, finally, black shoes. I admit I was shaken, but being a person of iron nerve in facing such phenomena I continued to play "Yankee Doodle." In spite of this counter-attraction, toward which all four boys turned uneasy glances, I held my audience. The Black Spectre, with a black book under its arm, drew nearer. Still I continued to play and nod my head and tap my toe. I felt like some modern Pied Piper piping away the children of these modern hills — piping them away from older people who could not understand them.

I could see an accusing look on the Spectre's face. I don't know what put it into my head, and I had no sooner said it than I was sorry for my levity, but the figure with the sad garments there in the matchless and triumphant spring day affected me with a curious sharp impatience. Had any one the right to look out so dolefully upon such a day and such a scene of simple happiness as this? So I took my whistle from my lips and asked:

"Is God dead?"

I shall never forget the indescribable look of horror and astonishment that swept over the young man's face.

"What do you mean, sir?" he asked with an air of stern authority which surprised me. His calling for the moment lifted him above himself: it was the Church which spoke.

I was on my feet in an instant, regretting the pain I had given him; and yet it seemed worth while now, having made my inadvertent remark, to show him frankly what lay in my mind. Such things sometimes help men.

"I meant no offence, sir," I said, "and I apologize for my flummery, but when I saw you coming up the hill, looking so gloomy and disconsolate on this bright day, as though you disapproved of God's world, the question slipped out before I knew it."

My words evidently struck deep down into some disturbed inner consciousness, for he asked — and his words seemed to slip out before he thought:

"Is *that* the way I impressed you?"

I found my heart going out strongly toward him. "Here," I thought to myself, "is a man in trouble."

I took a good long look at him. He was still a young man, though worn-looking — and sad, as I now saw it, rather than gloomy — with the sensitive lips and the unworldly look one sees sometimes in the faces of saints. His black coat was immaculately neat, but the worn button-covers and the shiny lapels told their own eloquent story. Oh, it seemed to me I knew him as well as if every incident of his life were written plainly upon his high, pale forehead! I have lived long in a country neighbourhood, and I knew him — poor flagellant of the rural church — I knew how he groaned under the sins of a community too comfortably willing to cast all its burdens on the Lord, or on the Lord's accredited local representative I inferred also the usual large family and the low salary (scandalously unpaid) and the frequent moves from place to place.

Unconsciously heaving a sigh the young man turned partly aside and said to me in a low, gentle voice:

"You are detaining my boys from church."

"I am very sorry," I said, "and I will detain them no longer," and with that I put aside my whistle, took up my bag and moved down the hill with them.

"The fact is," I said, "when I heard your bell I thought of going to church myself."

"Did you?" he asked eagerly. "Did you?"

I could see that my proposal of going to church had instantly affected his spirits. Then he hesitated abruptly with a sidelong glance at my bag and rusty clothing. I could see exactly what was passing in his mind.

"No," I said, smiling, as though answering a spoken question, "I am not exactly what you would call a tramp."

He flushed.

"I didn't mean — I *want* you to come. That's what a church is for. If I thought ——"

But he did not tell me what he thought; and, though he walked quietly at my side, he was evidently deeply disturbed. Something of his discouragement I sensed even then, and I don't think I was ever sorrier for a man in my life than I was for him at

that moment. Talk about the sufferings of
sinners! I wonder if they are to be compared with the trials of the saints?

So we approached the little white church,
and caused, I am certain, a tremendous
sensation. Nowhere does the unpredictable,
the unusual, excite such confusion as in that
settled institution — the church.

I left my bag in the vestibule, where I
have no doubt it was the object of much
inquiring and suspicious scrutiny, and took
my place in a convenient pew. It was a
small church with an odd air of domesticity,
and the proportion of old ladies and children
in the audience was pathetically large. As
a ruddy, vigorous, out-of-door person, with
the dust of life upon him, I felt distinctly
out of place.

I could pick out easily the Deacon, the
Old Lady Who Brought Flowers, the Presi-
dent of the Sewing Circle, and, above all,
the Chief Pharisee, sitting in his high place.
The Chief Pharisee — his name I learned
was Nash, Mr. J. H. Nash (I did not know
then that I was soon to make his acquaintance) — the Chief Pharisee looked as hard
as nails, a middle-aged man with stiff white

chin-whiskers, small, round, sharp eyes, and a pugnacious jaw.

"That man," said I to myself, "runs this church," and instantly I found myself looking upon him as a sort of personification of the troubles I had seen in the minister's eyes.

I shall not attempt to describe the service in detail. There was a discouraging droop and quaver in the singing, and the mournful-looking deacon who passed the collection-plate seemed inured to disappointment. The prayer had in it a note of despairing appeal which fell like a cold hand upon one's living soul. It gave one the impression that this was indeed a miserable, dark, despairing world, which deserved to be wrathfully destroyed, and that this miserable world was full of equally miserable, broken, sinful, sickly people.

The sermon was a little better, for somewhere hidden within him this pale young man had a spark of the divine fire, but it was so dampened by the atmosphere of the church that it never rose above a pale luminosity.

I found the service indescribably depressing. I had an impulse to rise up and cry out — almost anything to shock these people into opening their eyes upon real life. Indeed, though I hesitate about setting it down here, I was filled for some time with the liveliest imaginings of the following serio-comic enterprise:

I would step up the aisle, take my place in front of the Chief Pharisee, wag my finger under his nose, and tell him a thing or two about the condition of the church.

"The only live thing here," I would tell him, "is the spark in that pale minister's soul; and you're doing your best to smother that."

And I fully made up my mind that when he answered back in his chief-pharisaical way I would gently but firmly remove him from his seat, shake him vigorously two or three times (men's souls have often been saved with less!), deposit him flat in the aisle, and — yes — stand on him while I elucidated the situation to the audience at large. While I confined this amusing and interesting project to the humours of the imagination I am still convinced that something of the sort would have helped enormously in clearing up the religious and moral atmosphere of the place.

I had a wonderful sensation of relief when at last I stepped out again into the clear afternoon sunshine and got a reviving glimpse of the smiling green hills and the quiet fields and the sincere trees — and felt the welcome of the friendly road.

I would have made straight for the hills, but the thought of that pale minister held me back, and I waited quietly there under the trees till he came out. He was plainly looking for me, and asked me to wait and walk along with him, at which his four boys, whose acquaintance I had made under such thrilling circumstances earlier in the day, seemed highly delighted, and waited with me under the tree and told me a hundred important things about a certain calf, a pig, a kite, and other things at home.

Arriving at the minister's gate, I was invited in with a whole-heartedness that was altogether charming. The minister's wife, a faded-looking woman who had once possessed a delicate sort of prettiness, was waiting for us on the steps with a fine chubby baby on her arm — number five.

The home was much the sort of place I had imagined — a small house undesirably located (but cheap!), with a few straggling acres of garden and meadow upon which the minister and his boys were trying with inexperienced hands to piece out their inadequate living. At the very first glimpse of the garden I wanted to throw off my coat and go at it.

And yet — and yet — what a wonderful thing love is! There was, after all, something incalculable, something pervasively beautiful about this poor household. The moment the minister stepped inside his own door he became a different and livelier person. Something boyish crept into his manner, and a new look came into the eyes of his faded wife that made her almost pretty again. And the fat, comfortable baby rolled and gurgled about on the floor as happily as though there had been two nurses and a governess to look after him. As for the four boys, I have never seen healthier or happier ones.

I sat with them at their Sunday-evening luncheon. As the minister bowed his head to say grace I felt him clasp my hand on

one side while the oldest boy clasped my
hand on the other, and thus, linked together,
and accepting the stranger utterly, the family
looked up to God.

There was a fine, modest gayety about
the meal. In front of Mrs. Minister stood
a very large yellow bowl filled with what
she called rusk — a preparation unfamiliar
to me, made by browning and crushing the
crusts of bread and then rolling them down
into a coarse meal. A bowl of this, with
sweet, rich, yellow milk (for they kept their
own cow), made one of the most appetizing
dishes that ever I ate. It was downright
good: it gave one the unalloyed aroma of the
sweet new milk and the satisfying taste of the
crisp bread.

Nor have I ever enjoyed a more perfect
hospitality. I have been in many a richer
home where there was not a hundredth part
of the true gentility — the gentility of unapolo-
gizing simplicity and kindness.

And after it was over and cleared away
— the minister himself donning a long apron
and helping his wife — and the chubby
baby put to bed, we all sat around the table
in the gathering twilight.

I think men perish sometimes from sheer untalked talk. For lack of a creative listener they gradually fill up with unexpressed emotion. Presently this emotion begins to ferment, and finally — bang! — they blow up, burst, disappear in thin air. In all that community I suppose there was no one but the little faded wife to whom the minister dared open his heart, and I think he found me a godsend. All I really did was to look from one to the other and put in here and there an inciting comment or ask an understanding question. After he had told me his situation and the difficulties which confronted him and his small church, he exclaimed suddenly:

"A minister should by rights be a leader not only inside of his church, but outside of it in the community."

"You are right," I exclaimed with great earnestness; "you are right."

And with that I told him of our own Scotch preacher and how he led and moulded our community; and as I talked I could see him actually growing, unfolding, under my eyes.

"Why," said I, "you not only ought to

be the moral leader of this community, but you are!"

"That's what I tell him," exclaimed his wife.

"But he persists in thinking, doesn't he, that he is a poor sinner?"

"He thinks it too much," she laughed.

"Yes, yes," he said, as much to himself as to us, "a minister ought to be a fighter!"

It was beautiful, the boyish flush which now came into his face and the light that came into his eyes. I should never have identified him with the Black Spectre of the afternoon.

"Why," said I, " you *are* a fighter; you're fighting the greatest battle in the world to-day — the only real battle — the battle for the spiritual view of life."

Oh, I knew exactly what was the trouble with his religion — at least the religion which, under the pressure of that church, he felt obliged to preach! It was the old, groaning, denying, resisting religion. It was the sort of religion which sets a man apart and assures him that the entire universe in the guise of the Powers of Darkness is leagued against him. What he needed was a reviving draught

of the new faith which affirms, accepts, re-
joices, which feels the universe triumphantly
behind it. And so whenever the minister
told me what he ought to be — for he too
sensed the new impulse — I merely told him
he was just that. He needed only this little
encouragment to unfold.

"Yes," said he again, "I am the real moral
leader here."

At this I saw Mrs. Minister nodding her
head vigorously.

"It's you," she said, "and not Mr. Nash,
who should lead this community."

How a woman loves concrete applications!
She is your only true pragmatist. If a philosophy will not work, says she, why bother
with it?

The minister rose quickly from his chair,
threw back his head, and strode quickly up
and down the room.

"You are right," said he; "and I *will*
lead it. I'll have my farmers' meetings as I
planned."

It may have been the effect of the lamp-
light, but it seemed to me that little Mrs.
Minister, as she glanced up at him, looked
actually pretty.

The minister continued to stride up and down the room with his chin in the air.

"Mr. Nash," said she in a low voice to me, "is always trying to hold him down and keep him back. My husband *wants* to do the great things" —— wistfully.

"By every right," the minister was repeating quite oblivious of our presence, "I should lead this people."

"He sees the weakness of the church," she continued, "as well as any one, and he wants to start some vigorous community work — have agricultural meetings and boys' clubs, and lots of things like that — but Mr. Nash says it is no part of a minister's work: that it cheapens religion. He says that when a parson — Mr. Nash always calls him parson, and I just *loathe* that name — has preached, and prayed, and visited the sick, that's enough for *him*."

At this very moment a step sounded upon the walk, and an instant later a figure appeared in the doorway.

"Why, Mr. Nash," exclaimed little Mrs. Minister, exhibiting that astonishing gift of swift recovery which is the possession of even the simplest women, "come right in."

It was some seconds before the minister could come down from the heights and greet Mr. Nash. As for me, I was never more interested in my life.

"Now," said I to myself, "we shall see Christian meet Apollyon."

As soon as Mrs. Minister lighted the lamp I was introduced to the great man. He looked at me sharply with his small, round eyes, and said:

"Oh, you are the — the man who was in church this afternoon."

I admitted it, and he looked around at the minister with an accusing expression. He evidently did not approve of me, nor could I wholly blame him, for I knew well how he, as a rich farmer, must look upon a rusty man of the road like me. I should have liked dearly to cross swords with him myself, but greater events were imminent.

In no time at all the discussion, which had evidently been broken off at some previous meeting, concerning the proposed farmers' assembly at the church, had taken on a really lively tone. Mr. Nash was evidently in the somewhat irritable mood with which important people may sometimes indulge themselves, for he bit off his words in a way that was calculated to make any but an unusually meek and saintly man exceedingly uncomfortable. But the minister, with the fine, high humility of those whose passion is for great or true things, was quite oblivious to the harsh words. Borne along by an irresistible enthusiasm, he told in glowing terms what his plan would mean to the community, how the people needed a new social and civic spirit — a "neighbourhood religious feeling" he called it. And as he talked, his face flushed and his eyes shone with the pure fire of a great purpose. But I could see that all this enthusiasm impressed the practical Mr. Nash as mere moonshine. He grew more and more uneasy. Finally he brought his hand down with a resounding thwack upon his knee, and said in a high, cutting voice:

"I don't believe in any such newfangled nonsense. It ain't none of a parson's business what the community does. You're hired, ain't you, an' paid to run the church? That's the end of it. We ain't goin' to have any mixin' of religion an' farmin' in *this* neighbourhood."

My eyes were on the pale man of God. I felt as though a human soul were being weighed in the balance. What would he do now? What was he worth *really* as a man as well as a minister?

He paused a moment with downcast eyes. I saw little Mrs. Minister glance at him — once — wistfully. He rose from his place, drew himself up to his full height — I shall not soon forget the look on his face — and uttered these amazing words:

"Martha, bring the ginger-jar."

Mrs. Minister, without a word, went to a little cupboard on the farther side of the room and took down a brown earthenware jar, which she brought over and placed on the table, Mr. Nash following her movements with astonished eyes. No one spoke.

The minister took the jar in his hands as he might the communion-cup just before saying the prayer of the sacrament.

"Mr. Nash," said he in a loud voice, "I've decided to hold that farmers' meeting."

Before Mr. Nash could reply the minister seated himself and was pouring out the contents of the jar upon the table — a clatter of dimes, nickels, pennies, a few quarters and half dollars, and a very few bills.

"Martha, just how much money is there here?"

"Twenty-four dollars and sixteen cents."

The minister put his hand into his pocket and, after counting out certain coins, said:

"Here's one dollar and eighty-four cents more. That makes twenty-six dollars. Now, Mr. Nash, you're the largest contributor to my salary in this neighbourhood. You gave twenty-six dollars last year — fifty cents a week. It is a generous contribution, but I cannot take it any longer. It is fortunate that my wife has saved up this money to buy a sewing-machine, so that we can pay back your contribution in full."

He paused; no one of us spoke a word.

"Mr. Nash," he continued, and his face was good to see, "I am the minister here. I am convinced that what the community needs is more of a religious and social spirit, and I am going about getting it in the way the Lord leads me."

At this I saw Mrs. Minister look up at her husband with such a light in her eyes as any man might well barter his life for

— I could not keep my own eyes from the pure beauty of it.

I knew too what this defiance meant. It meant that this little family was placing its all upon the altar — even the pitiful coins for which they had skimped and saved for months for a particular purpose. Talk of the heroism of the men who charged with Pickett at Gettysburg! Here was a courage higher and whiter than that; here was a courage that dared to fight alone.

As for Mr. Nash, the face of that Chief Pharisee was a study. Nothing is so paralyzing to a rich man as to find suddenly that his money will no longer command him any advantage. Like all hard-shelled, practical people, Mr. Nash could only dominate in a world which recognized the same material supremacy that he recognized. Any one who insisted upon flying was lost to Mr. Nash.

The minister pushed the little pile of coins toward him.

"Take it, Mr. Nash," said he.

At that Mr. Nash rose hastily.

"I will not," he said gruffly.

He paused, and looked at the minister with a strange expression in his small round eyes — was it anger, or was it fear, or could it have been admiration?

"If you want to waste your time on fiddlin' farmers' meetings — a man that knows

" HE TURNED, REACHED FOR HIS HAT, AND THEN WENT
OUT OF THE DOOR INTO THE DARKNESS "

as little of farmin' as you do — why, go ahead for all o' me.   But don't count me in."

He turned, reached for his hat, and then went out of the door into the darkness.

For a moment we all sat perfectly silent, then the minister rose, and said solemnly:

"Martha, let's sing something."

Martha crossed the room to the cottage organ and seated herself on the stool.

"What shall we sing?" said she.

"Something with fight in it, Martha," he responded; "something with plenty of fight in it."

So we sang "Onward, Christian Soldiers, Marching as to War," and followed that up with:

> Awake, my soul, stretch every nerve
> And press with vigour on;
> A heavenly race demands thy zeal
> And an immortal crown.

When we had finished, and as Martha rose from her seat, the minister impulsively put his hands on her shoulders, and said:

"Martha, this is the greatest night of my life."

He took a turn up and down the room, and then with an exultant boyish laugh said:

"We'll go to town to-morrow and pick out that sewing-machine!"

I remained with them that night and part of the following day, taking a hand with them in the garden, but of the events of that day I shall speak in another chapter.

I PLAY THE PART OF A SPECTACLE PEDDLER

CHAPTER V

I PLAY THE PART OF A SPECTACLE-
PEDDLER

YESTERDAY was exactly the sort of a
day I love best — a spicy, unexpected,
amusing day — a day crowned with a droll
adventure.

I cannot at all account for it, but it seems
to me I take the road each morning with a
livelier mind and keener curiosity. If you
were to watch me narrowly these days
you would see that I am slowly shedding

my years. I suspect that some one of the clear hill streams from which I have been drinking (lying prone on my face) was in reality the fountain of eternal youth. I shall not go back to see.

It seems to me, when I feel like this, that in every least thing upon the roadside, or upon the hill, lurks the stuff of adventure. What a world it is! A mile south of here I shall find all that Stanley found in the jungles of Africa; a mile north I am Peary at the Pole!

You there, brown-clad farmer on the tall seat of your wagon, driving townward with a red heifer for sale, I can show you that life — your life — is not all a gray smudge, as you think it is, but crammed, packed, loaded with miraculous things. I can show you wonders past belief in your own soul. I can easily convince you that you are in reality a poet, a hero, a true lover, a saint.

It is because we are not humble enough in the presence of the divine daily fact that adventure knocks so rarely at our door. A thousand times I have had to learn this truth (what lesson so hard to learn as the lesson of humility!) and I suppose I shall have to learn it a thousand times more. This very day, straining my eyes to see the distant wonders of the mountains, I nearly missed a miracle by the roadside.

Soon after leaving the minister and his family — I worked with them in their garden with great delight most of the forenoon — I came, within a mile to the wide white turnpike — the Great Road.

Now, I usually prefer the little roads, the little, unexpected, curving, leisurely country roads. The sharp hills, the pleasant deep valleys, the bridges not too well kept, the verdure deep grown along old fences, the houses opening hospitably at the very roadside, all these things I love. They come to me with the same sort of charm and flavour, only vastly magnified, which I find often in the essays of the older writers — those leisurely old fellows who took time to write, *really* write. The important thing to me about a road, as about life and literature, is not that it goes anywhere, but that it is livable while it goes. For if I were to arrive — and who knows that I ever shall arrive? — I think I should be no happier than I am here.

Thus I have commonly avoided the Great White Road — the broad, smooth turnpike — rock-bottomed and rolled by a beneficent State — without so much as a loitering curve to whet one's curiosity, nor a thank-you-ma'am to laugh over, nor a sinful hill to test your endurance — not so much as a dreamy valley! It pursues its hard, unshaded, practical way directly from some particular place to some other particular place — and from time to time a motor-car shoots in at one end of it and out at the other, leaving its dust to settle upon quiet travellers like me.

Thus to-day when I came to the turnpike I was at first for making straight across it and taking to the hills beyond, but at that very moment a motor-car whirled past me as I stood there, and a girl with a merry face waved her hand at me. I lifted my hat in return, and as I watched them out of sight I felt a curious new sense of warmth and friendliness there in the Great Road.

"These are just people, too," I said aloud — "and maybe they really like it!" .

And with that I began laughing at myself, and at the whole big, amazing, interesting world. Here was I pitying them for their

"*I usually prefer the little roads, the little, unexpected, curving, leisurely country roads.*"

benighted state, and there were they, no doubt, pitying me for mine!

And with that pleasant and satisfactory thought in my mind and a song in my throat I swung into the Great Road.

"It doesn't matter in the least," said I to myself, "whether a man takes hold of life by the great road or the little ones so long as he takes hold."

And oh, it was a wonderful day! A day with movement in it; a day that flowed! In every field the farmers were at work, the cattle fed widely in the meadows, and the Great Road itself was alive with a hundred varied sorts of activity. Light winds stirred the tree-tops and rippled in the new grass; and from the thickets I heard the blackbirds crying. Everything animate and inanimate, that morning, seemed to have its own clear voice and to cry out at me for my interest, or curiosity, or sympathy. Under such circumstances it could not have been long — nor was it long — before I came plump upon the first of a series of odd adventures.

A great many people, I know, abominate the roadside sign. It seems to them a desecration of nature, the intrusion of rude commercialism upon the perfection of natural beauty. But not I. I have no such feeling. Oh, the signs in themselves are often rude and unbeautiful, and I never wished my own barn or fences to sing the praises of swamproot or sarsaparilla — and yet there is something wonderfully human about these painted and pasted vociferations of the road-side signs; and I don't know why they are less "natural" in their way than a house or barn or a planted field of corn. They also tell us about life. How eagerly they cry out at us, "Buy me, buy me!" What enthusiasm they have in their own concerns, what boundless faith in themselves! How they speak of the enormous energy, activity, resourcefulness of human kind!

Indeed, I like all kinds of signs. The autocratic warnings of the road, the musts and the must-nots of traffic, I observe in passing; and I often stand long at the cross-ings and look up at the finger-posts, and consider my limitless wealth as a traveller. By this road I may, at my own pleasure, reach the Great City; by that — who knows? — the far wonders of Cathay. And I respond always to the appeal which the devoted pilgrim paints on the rocks at the roadside: "Repent ye, for the kingdom of God is at hand," and though I am certain that the kingdom of God is already here, I stop always and repent — just a little — knowing that there is always room for it. At the entrance of the little towns, also, or in the squares of the villages, I stop often to read the signs of taxes assessed, or of political meetings; I see the evidences of homes broken up in the notices of auction sales, and of families bereaved in the dry and formal publications of the probate court. I pause, too, before the signs of amusements flaming red and yellow on the barns (boys, the circus is coming to town!), and I pause also, but no longer, to read the silent signs carved in stone .in the little cemeteries as I pass. Symbols, you say? Why, they're the very stuff of life. If you cannot see life here in the wide road, you will never see it at all.

Well, I saw a sign yesterday at the roadside that I never saw anywhere before. It was not a large sign — indeed rather inconspicuous — consisting of a single word rather crudely painted in black (as by an amateur) upon a white board. It was nailed to a tree where those in swift passing cars could not avoid seeing it:

REST

I cannot describe the odd sense of enliven-ment, of pleasure I had when I saw this new sign.

"Rest!" I exclaimed aloud. "Indeed I will," and I sat down on a stone not far away. "Rest!"

What a sign for this very spot! Here in the midst of the haste and hurry of the Great Road a quiet voice was saying, "Rest." Some one with imagination, I thought, evi-dently put that up; some quietist offering this mild protest against the breathless prog-ress of the age. How often I have felt the same way myself — as though I were being swept onward through life faster than I could well enjoy it. For nature passes the dishes far more rapidly than we can help ourselves.

Or perhaps, thought I, eagerly speculating, this may be only some cunning advertiser with rest for sale (in these days
even rest has its price), thus piquing the
curiosity of the traveller for the disclosure
which he will make a mile or so farther on.
Or else some humourist wasting his wit upon
the Fraternity of the Road, too willing (like
me, perhaps) to accept his ironical advice.
But it would be well worth while, should I
find him, to see him chuckle behind his hand.

So I sat there, very much interested, for
a long time, even framing a rather amusing picture in my own mind of the sort of
person who painted these signs, deciding
finally that he must be a zealot rather than
a trader or humourist. (Confidentially, I
could not make a picture of him in which he
was not endowed with plentiful long hair!)
As I walked onward again, I decided that
in any guise I should like to see him, and I
enjoyed thinking what I should say if I
met him. A mile farther up the road I
saw another sign exactly like the first.

"Here he is again," I said exultantly,
and that sign being somewhat nearer the
ground I was able to examine it carefully

front and back, but it bore no evidence of its origin.

In the next few miles I saw two other signs with nothing on them but the single word "Rest."

Now this excellent admonition — like much of the excellent admonition in this world — affected me perversely: it made me more restless than ever. I felt that I could not rest properly until I found out who wanted me to rest, and why. It opened indeed a limitless vista for new adventure.

Presently, away ahead of me in the road, I saw a man standing near a one-horse wagon. He seemed to be engaged in some activity near the roadside, but I could not tell exactly what. As I hastened nearer I discovered that he was a short, strongly built, sun-bronzed man in working-clothes — and with the shortest of short hair. I saw him take a shovel from the wagon and begin digging. He was the road-worker.

I asked the road-worker if he had seen the curious signs. He looked up at me with a broad smile (he had good-humoured, very bright blue eyes).

"Yes," he said, "but they ain't for me."

"Then you don't follow the advice they give?"

"Not with a section like mine," said he, and he straightened up and looked first one way of the road and then the other. "I have from Grabow Brook, but not the bridge, to the top o' Sullivan Hill, and all the culverts between, though two of 'em are by rights bridges. And I claim that's a job for any full-grown man."

He began shovelling again in the road as if to prove how busy he was. There had been a small landslide from an open cut on one side and a mass of gravel and small boulders lay scattered on the smooth macadam. I watched him for a moment. I love to watch the motions of vigorous men at work, the easy play of the muscles, the swing of the shoulders, the vigour of stoutly planted legs. He evidently considered the conversation closed, and I, as — well, as a dusty man of the road — easily dismissed. (You have no idea, until you try it, what a weight of prejudice the man of the road has to surmount before he is accepted on easy terms by the ordinary members of the human race.)

A few other well-intentioned observations on my part having elicited nothing but monosyllabic replies, I put my bag down by the roadside and, going up to the wagon, got out a shovel, and without a word took my place at the other end of the landslide and began to shovel for all I was worth.

I said not a word to the husky road-worker and pretended not to look at him, but I saw him well enough out of the corner of my eye. He was evidently astonished and interested, as I knew he would be: it was something entirely new on the road. He didn't quite know whether to be angry, or amused, or sociable. I caught him looking over at me several times, but I offered no response; then he cleared his throat and said:

"Where you from?"

I answered with a monosyllable which I knew he could not quite catch. Silence again for some time, during which I shovelled valiantly and with great inward amusement. Oh, there is nothing like cracking a hard human nut! I decided at that moment to have him invite me to supper.

Finally, when I showed no signs of stopping

my work, he himself paused and leaned on his shovel. I kept right on.

"Say, partner," said he, finally, "did *you* read those signs as you come up the road?"

"Yes," I said, "but they weren't for me, either. My section's a long one, too."

"Say, you ain't a road-worker, are you?" he asked eagerly.

"Yes," said I, with a sudden inspiration, "that's exactly what I am — a road-worker."

"Put her there, then, partner," he said, with a broad smile on his bronzed face.

He and I struck hands, rested on our shovels (like old hands at it), and looked with understanding into each other's eyes. We both knew the trade and the tricks of the trade; all bars were down between us. The fact is, we had both seen and profited by the peculiar signs at the roadside.

"Where's your section?" he asked easily.

"Well," I responded after considering the question, "I have a very long and hard section. It begins at a place called Prosy Common — do you know it? — and reaches to the top of Clear Hill. There are several bad spots on the way, I can tell you."

"Don't know it," said the husky road-worker; "'tain't round here, is it? In the town of Sheldon, maybe?"

Just at this moment, perhaps fortunately, for there is nothing so difficult to satisfy as the appetite of people for specific informa-tion, a motor-car whizzed past, the driver holding up his hand in greeting, and the road-worker and I responding in accord with the etiquette of the Great Road.

"There he goes in the ruts again," said the husky road-worker. "Why is it, I'd like to know, that every one wants to run in the same *i*-dentical track when they've got the whole wide road before 'em?"

"That's what has long puzzled me, too," I said. "Why *will* people continue to run in ruts?"

"It don't seem to do no good to put up signs," said the road-worker.

"Very little indeed," said I. "The fact is, people have got to be bumped out of most of the ruts they get into."

"You're right," said he enthusiastically, and his voice dropped into the tone of one speaking to a member of the inner guild. "I know how to get 'em."

A MOTOR-CAR WHIZZED PAST. "THERE HE GOES IN THE
RUTS AGAIN," SAID THE HUSKY ROAD-WORKER

"How?" I asked in an equally mysterious voice.

"I put a stone or two in the ruts!"

"Do you?" I exclaimed. "I've done that very thing myself — many a time! Just place a good hard tru — I mean stone, with a bit of common dust sprinkled over it, in the middle of the rut, and they'll look out for *that* rut for some time to come."

"Ain't it gorgeous," said the husky road-worker, chuckling joyfully, "to see 'em bump?"

"It is," said I — "gorgeous."

After that, shovelling part of the time in a leisurely way, and part of the time responding to the urgent request of the signs by the roadside (it pays to advertise!), the husky road-worker and I discussed many great and important subjects, all, however, curiously related to roads. Working all day long with his old horse, removing obstructions, draining out the culverts, filling ruts and holes with new stone, and repairing the damage of rain and storm, the road-worker was filled with a world of practical information covering roads and road-making. And having learned that I was of the same calling

we exchanged views with the greatest enthusiasm.   It was astonishing to see how nearly
in agreement we were as to what constituted
an ideal road.

"Almost everything," said he, "depends
on depth.   If you get a good solid foundation,
the' ain't anything that can break up your
road."

"Exactly what I have discovered," I responded.   "Get down to bedrock and do an
honest job of building."

"And don't have too many sharp turns."

"No," said I, "long, leisurely curves are
best — all through life.   You have observed
that nearly all the accidents on the road are
due to sharp turnings."

"Right you are!" he exclaimed.

"A man who tries to turn too sharply on
his way nearly always skids."

"Or else turns turtle in the ditch."

But it was not until we reached the subject
of oiling that we mounted to the real summit
of enthusiastic agreement.   Of all things
on the road, or above the road, or in the
waters under the road, there is nothing that
the road-worker dislikes more than oil.

"It's all right," said he, "to use oil for

surfacin' and to keep down the dust. You don't need much and it ain't messy. But sometimes when you see oil pumped on a road, you know that either the contractor has been jobbin', or else the road's worn out and ought to be rebuilt."

"That's exactly what I've found," said I. "Let a road become almost impassable with ruts and rocks and dust, and immediately some man says, 'Oh, it's all right — put on a little oil ——'"

"That's what our supervisor is always sayin'," said the road-worker.

"Yes," I responded, "it usually is the supervisor. He lives by it. He wants to smooth over the defects, he wants to lay the dust that every passerby kicks up, he tries to smear over the truth regarding conditions with messy and ill-smelling oil. Above everything, he doesn't want the road dug up and rebuilt — says it will interfere with traffic, injure business, and even set people to talking about changing the route entirely! Oh, haven't I seen it in religion, where they are doing their best to oil up roads that are entirely worn out — and as for politics, is not the cry of the party-roadster and the harmony-oilers abroad in the land?"

In the excited interest with which this idea now bore me along I had entirely forgotten the existence of my companion, and as I now glanced at him I saw him standing with a curious look of astonishment and suspicion on his face. I saw that I had unintentionally gone a little too far. So I said abruptly:

"Partner, let's get a drink. I'm thirsty."

He followed me, I thought a bit reluctantly, to a little brook not far up the road where we had been once before. As we were drinking, silently, I looked at the stout young fellow standing there, and I thought to myself:

What a good, straightforward young fellow he is anyway, and how thoroughly he knows his job. I thought how well he was equipped with unilluminated knowledge, and it came to me whimsically, that here was a fine bit of road-mending for me to do.

Most people have sight, but few have insight; and as I looked into the clear blue eyes of my friend I had a sudden swift inspiration, and before I could repent of it I had said to him in the most serious voice that I could command:

"Friend, I am in reality a spectacle-peddler ——"

His glance shifted uncomfortably to my gray bag.

"And I want to sell you a pair of spectacles," I said. "I see that you are nearly blind."

"Me blind!"

It would be utterly impossible to describe the expression on his face. His hand went involuntarily to his eyes, and he glanced quickly, somewhat fearfully, about.

"Yes, nearly blind," said I. "I saw it when I first met you. You don't know it yourself yet, but I can assure you it is a bad case."

I paused, and shook my head slowly. If I had not been so much in earnest, I think I should have been tempted to laugh outright. I had begun my talk with him half jestingly, with the amusing idea of breaking through his shell, but I now found myself tremendously engrossed, and desiring nothing in the world (at that moment) so much as to make him see what I saw. I felt as though I held a live human soul in my hand.

"Say, partner," said the road-worker, "are you sure you aren't ——" He tapped his forehead and began to edge away.

I did not answer his question at all, but continued, with my eyes fixed on him:

"It is a peculiar sort of blindness. Apparently, as you look about, you see everything there is to see, but as a matter of fact you see nothing in the world but this road——"

"It's time that I was seein' it again then," said he, making as if to turn back to work, but remaining with a disturbed expression on his countenance.

"The spectacles I have to sell," said I, "are powerful magnifiers" — he glanced again at the gray bag. "When you put them on you will see a thousand wonderful things besides the road ——"

"Then you ain't a road-worker after all!" he said, evidently trying to be bluff and outright with me.

Now your substantial, sober, practical American will stand only about so much verbal foolery; and there is nothing in the world that makes him more uncomfortable — yes, downright mad! — than to feel that he is being played with. I could see that I had nearly reached the limit with him, and that if I held him now it must be by driving the truth straight home.   So I stepped over toward him and said very earnestly:

"My friend, don't think I am merely joking you. I was never more in earnest in all my life. When I told you I was a road-worker I meant it, but I had in mind the mending of other kinds of roads than this."

I laid my hand on his arm, and explained to him as directly and simply as English words could do it, how, when he had spoken of oil for his roads, I thought of another sort of oil for another sort of roads, and when he spoke of curves in his roads I was thinking of curves in the roads I dealt with, and I explained to him what my roads were. I have never seen a man more intensely interested: he neither moved nor took his eyes from my face.

"And when I spoke of selling you a pair of spectacles," said I, "it was only a way of telling you how much I wanted to make you see my kinds of roads as well as your own."

I paused, wondering if, after all, he could be made to see. I know now how the surgeon must feel at the crucial moment of his accomplished operation. Will the patient live or die?

The road-worker drew a long breath as he came out from under the anesthetic.

"I guess, partner," said he, "you're trying to put a stone or two in my ruts!"

I had him!

"Exactly," I exclaimed eagerly.

We both paused. He was the first to speak — with some embarrassment:

"Say, you're just like a preacher I used to know when I was a kid. He was always sayin' things that meant something else, and when you found out what he was drivin' at you always felt kind of queer in your insides."

I laughed.

"It's a mighty good sign," I said, "when a man begins to feel queer in the insides. It shows that something is happening to him."

With that we walked back to the road,

feeling very close and friendly — and began shovelling again, not saying much. After quite a time, when we had nearly cleaned up the landslide, I heard the husky road-worker chuckling to himself; finally, straightening up, he said:

"Say, there's more things in a road than ever I dreamt of."

"I see," said I, "that the new spectacles are a good fit."

The road-worker laughed long and loud.

"You're a good one, all right," he said. "I see what *you* mean. I catch your point."

"And now that you've got them on," said I, "and they are serving you so well, I'm not going to sell them to you at all. I'm going to present them to you — for I haven't seen anybody in a long time that I've enjoyed meeting more than I have you."

We nurse a fiction that people love to cover up their feelings; but I have learned that if the feeling is real and deep they love far better to find a way to uncover it.

"Same here," said the road-worker simply, but with a world of genuine feeling in his voice.

Well, when it came time to stop work

the road-worker insisted that I get in and go home with him.

"I want you to see my wife and kids," said he.

The upshot of it was that I not only remained for supper — and a good supper it was — but I spent the night in his little home, close at the side of the road near the foot of a fine hill. And from time to time all night long, it seemed to me, I could hear the rush of cars going by in the smooth road outside, and sometimes their lights flashed in at my window, and sometimes I heard them sound their brassy horns.

I wish I could tell more of what I saw there, of the garden back of the house, and of all the road-worker and his wife told me of their simple history — but the road calls!

When I set forth early this morning the road-worker followed me out to the smooth macadam (his wife standing in the doorway with her hands rolled in her apron) and said to me, a bit shyly:

"I'll be more sort o' — sort o' interested in roads since I've seen you."

"I'll be along again some of these days," said I, laughing, "and I'll stop in and show you my new stock of spectacles. Maybe I can sell you another pair!"

"Maybe you kin," and he smiled a broad, understanding smile.

Nothing brings men together like having a joke in common.

So I walked off down the road — in the best of spirits — ready for the events of another day.

It will surely be a great adventure, one of these days, to come this way again — and to visit the Stanleys, and the Vedders, and the Minister, and drop in and sell another pair of specs to the Road-worker. It seems to me I have a wonderfully rosy future ahead of me!

P. S.—I have not yet found out who painted the curious signs; but I am not as uneasy about it as I was. I have seen two more of them already this morning — and find they exert quite a psychological influence.

AN EXPERIMENT IN HUMAN NATURE

CHAPTER VI

AN EXPERIMENT IN HUMAN NATURE

IN THE early morning after I left the husky
road-mender (wearing his new spectacles),
I remained steadfastly on the Great Road or
near it. It was a prime spring day, just a
little hazy, as though promising rain, but soft
and warm.

"They will be working in the garden at
home," I thought, "and there will be worlds
of rhubarb and asparagus." Then I remembered how the morning sunshine would look
on the little vine-clad back porch (reaching

halfway up the weathered door) of my own house among the hills.

It was the first time since my pilgrimage began that I had thought with any emotion of my farm — or of Harriet.

And then the road claimed me again, and I began to look out for some further explanation of the curious sign, the single word "Rest," which had interested me so keenly on the preceding day. It may seem absurd to some who read these lines — some practical people! — but I cannot convey the pleasure I had in the very elusiveness and mystery of the sign, nor how I wished I might at the next turn come upon the poet himself. I decided that no one but a poet could have contented himself with a lyric in one word, unless it might have been a humourist, to whom sometimes a single small word is more blessed than all the verbal riches of Webster himself. For it is nothing short of genius that uses one word when twenty will say the same thing!

Or, would he, after all, turn out to be only a more than ordinarily alluring advertiser? I confess my heart went into

my throat that morning, when I first saw
the sign, lest it read:

REST aurant 2 miles east

nor should I have been surprised if it had.

I caught a vicarious glimpse of the sign-
man to-day, through the eyes of a young
farmer. Yes, he s'posed he'd seen him,
he said; wore a slouch hat, couldn't tell
whether he was young or old. Drove into
the bushes (just daown there beyond
the brook) and, standin' on the seat of
his buggy, nailed something to a tree. A
day or two later — the dull wonder of man-
kind! — the young farmer, passing that way
to town, had seen the odd sign "Rest" on the
tree: he s'posed the fellow put it there.

"What does it mean?"

"Well, naow, I hadn't thought," said the
young farmer.

"Did the fellow by any chance have long
hair?"

"Well, naow, I didn't notice," said he.

"Are you sure he wore a slouch hat?"

"Ye-es — or it may a-been straw," replied the observant young farmer.

So I tramped that morning; and as I tramped I let my mind go out warmly to the people living all about on the farms or in the hills. It is pleasant at times to feel life, as it were, in general terms; no specific Mr. Smith or concrete Mr. Jones, but just human life. I love to think of people all around going out busily in the morning to their work and returning at night, weary, to rest. I like to think of them growing up, growing old, loving, achieving, sinning, failing — in short, living.

In such a live-minded mood as this it often happens that the most ordinary things appear charged with new significance. I suppose I had seen a thousand rural-mail boxes along country roads before that day, but I had seen them as the young farmer saw the sign-man. They were mere inert objects of iron and wood.

But as I tramped, thinking of the people in the hills, I came quite unexpectedly upon a sandy by-road that came out through a thicket of scrub oaks and hazel-brush,

like some shy countryman, to join the turnpike. As I stood looking into it — for
it seemed peculiarly inviting — I saw at
the entrance a familiar group of rural-mail
boxes. And I saw them not as dead things,
but for the moment — the illusion was overpowering — they were living, eager hands
outstretched to the passing throng. I could
feel, hear, see the farmers up there in the
hills reaching out to me, to all the world,
for a thousand inexpressible things, for more
life, more companionship, more comforts,
more money.

It occurred to me at that moment, whimsically and yet somehow seriously, that I
might respond to the appeal of the shy country road and the outstretched hands. At
first I did not think of anything I could do
— save to go up and eat dinner with one
of the hill farmers, which might not be an
unmixed blessing! — and then it came to me.

"I will write a letter!"

Straightway and with the liveliest amusement I began to formulate in my mind what
I should say:

DEAR FRIEND: You do not know me. I am a passerby in
the road. My name is David Grayson. You do not know

me, and it may seem odd to you to receive a letter from an entire stranger. But I am something of a farmer myself, and as I went by I could not help thinking of you and of your family and your farm. The fact is, I should like to look you up, and talk with you about many things. I myself cultivate a number of curious fields, and raise many kinds of crops ——

At this interesting point my inspiration suddenly collapsed, for I had a vision, at once amusing and disconcerting, of my hill farmer (and his practical wife!) receiving such a letter (along with the country paper, a circular advertising a cure for catarrh, and the most recent catalogue of the largest mail-order house in creation). I could see them standing there in their doorway, the man with his coat off, doubtfully scratching his head as he read my letter, the woman wiping her hands on her apron and looking over his shoulder, and a youngster squeezing between the two and demanding, "What is it, Paw?"

I found myself wondering how they would receive such an unusual letter, what they would take it to mean. And in spite of all I could do, I could imagine no expression on their faces save one of incredulity and suspicion. I could fairly see the shrewd,

worldly wise look come into the farmer's face;
I could hear him say:

"Ha, guess he thinks we ain't cut our
eye-teeth!"   And he would instantly begin
speculating as to whether this was a new
scheme for selling him second-rate nursery
stock, or the smooth introduction of another
sewing-machine agent.

Strange world, strange world!   Sometimes
it seems to me that the hardest thing of all
to believe in is simple friendship.   Is it not
a comment upon our civilization that it
is so often easier to believe that a man is a
friend-for-profit, or even a cheat, than that
he is frankly a well-wisher of his neighbours?

These reflections put such a damper upon
my enthusiasm that I was on the point of
taking again to the road, when it came to me
powerfully: Why not try the experiment?
Why not?

"Friendship," I said aloud, "is the greatest
thing in the world.   There is no door it will
not unlock, no problem it will not solve.   It
is, after all, the only real thing in this world."

The sound of my own voice brought me
suddenly to myself, and I found that I

was standing there in the middle of the public road, one clenched fist absurdly raised in air, delivering an oration to a congregation of rural-mail boxes!

And yet, in spite of the humorous aspects of the idea, it still appeared to me that such an experiment would not only fit in with the true object of my journeying, but that it might be full of amusing and interesting adventures. Straightway I got my note-book out of my bag and, sitting down near the roadside, wrote my letter. I wrote it as though my life depended upon it, with the intent of making some one household there in the hills feel at least a little wave of warmth and sympathy from the great world that was passing in the road below. I tried to prove the validity of a kindly thought with no selling device attached to it; I tried to make it such a word of frank companionship as I myself, working in my own fields, would like to receive.

Among the letter-boxes in the group was one that stood a little detached and behind the others, as though shrinking from such prosperous company. It was made of un-painted wood, with leather hinges, and looked shabby in comparison with the jaunty red, green, and gray paint of some of the other boxes (with their cocky little metallic flags upraised). It bore the good American name of Clark — T. N. Clark — and it seemed to me that I could tell something of the Clarks by the box at the crossing.

"I think they need a friendly word," I said to myself.

So I wrote the name T. N. Clark on my envelope and put the letter in his box.

It was with a sense of joyous adventure that I now turned aside into the sandy road and climbed the hill. My mind busied itself with thinking how I should carry out my experiment, how I should approach these Clarks, and how and what they were. A thousand ways I pictured to myself the receipt of the letter: it would at least be something new for them, something just a little disturbing, and I was curious to see whether it might open the rift of wonder wide enough to let me slip into their lives.

I have often wondered why it is that men should be so fearful of new ventures in social relationships, when I have found them so fertile, so enjoyable. Most of us fear (actually fear) people who differ from ourselves, either up or down the scale. Your Edison pries fearlessly into the most intimate secrets of matter; your Marconi employs the mysterious properties of the "jellied ether," but let a man seek to experiment with the laws of that singular electricity which connects you and me (though you be a millionaire and I a ditch-digger), and we think him a wild visionary, an academic person. I think sometimes that the science of humanity to-day is in about the state of darkness that the natural sciences were when Linnæus and Cuvier and Lamarck began groping for the great laws of natural unity. Most of the human race is still groaning under the belief that each of us is a special and unrelated creation, just as men for ages saw no relationships between the fowls of the air, the beasts of the field, and the fish of the sea. But, thank God, we are beginning to learn that unity is as much a law of life as selfish struggle, and love a more vital force than avarice or lust of power or place. A Wandering Carpenter knew it, and taught it, twenty centuries ago.

"The next house beyond the ridge," said the toothless old woman, pointing with a long finger, "is the Clarks'. You can't miss it," and I thought she looked at me oddly.

I had been walking briskly for some three miles, and it was with keen expectation that I now mounted the ridge and saw the farm for which I was looking, lying there in the valley before me. It was altogether a wild and beautiful bit of country — stunted cedars on the knolls of the rolling hills, a brook trailing its way among alders and willows down a long valley, and shaggy old fields smiling in the sun. As I came nearer I could see that the only disharmony in the valley was the work (or idleness) of men. A broken mowing-machine stood in the field where it had been left the summer before, rusty and forlorn, and dead weeds marked the edges of a field wherein the spring ploughing was now only half done. The whole farmstead, indeed, looked tired. As for the house and barn, they had reached that final stage of decay in which the best thing that could be said of them was that they were picturesque. Everything was as different from the farm of the energetic and joyous Stanleys, whose work I had shared only a few days before, as anything that could be imagined.

Now, my usual way of getting into step with people is simplicity itself. I take off my coat and go to work with them and the first thing I know we have become first-rate friends. One doesn't dream of the possibilities of companionship in labour until he has tried it.

But how shall one get into step with a man who is not stepping?

On the porch of the farmhouse, there in the mid-afternoon, a man sat idly; and children were at play in the yard. I went in at the gate, not knowing in the least what I should say or do, but determined to get hold of the problem somewhere. As I approached the step, I swung my bag from my shoulder.

"Don't want to buy nothin'," said the man.

"Well," said I, "that is fortunate, for I have nothing to sell. But you've got something I want."

He looked at me dully.

"What's that?"

"A drink of water."

Scarcely moving his head, he called to

" AS I STOOD THERE THE CHILDREN GATHERED CURIOUSLY
AROUND ME "

a shy older girl who had just appeared in the doorway.

"Mandy, bring a dipper of water."

As I stood there the children gathered

curiously around me, and the man continued to sit in his chair, saying absolutely nothing, a picture of dull discouragement.

"How they need something to stir them up," I thought.

When I had emptied the dipper, I sat down on the top step of the porch, and, without saying a word to the man, placed my bag beside me and began to open it. The shy girl paused, dipper in hand, the children stood on tiptoe, and even the man showed signs of curiosity. With studied deliberation I took out two books I had with me and put them on the porch; then I proceeded to rummage for a long time in the bottom of the bag as though I could not find what I wanted. Every eye was glued upon me, and I even heard the step of Mrs. Clark as she came to the doorway, but I did not look up or speak. Finally I pulled out my tin whistle and, leaning back against the porch column, placed it to my lips, and began playing in Tom Madison's best style (eyes half closed, one toe tapping to the music, head nodding, fingers lifted high from the stops), I began playing "Money Musk," and "Old Dan Tucker."

Oh, I put vim into it, I can tell you! And bad as my playing was, I had from the start an absorption of attention from my audience that Paderewski himself might have envied. I wound up with a lively trill in the high notes and took my whistle from my lips with a hearty laugh, for the whole thing had been downright good fun, the playing itself, the make-believe which went with it, the surprise and interest in the children's faces, the slow-breaking smile of the little girl with the dipper.

"I'll warrant you, madam," I said to the woman who now stood frankly in the doorway with her hands wrapped in her apron, "you haven't heard those tunes since you were a girl and danced to 'em."

"You're right," she responded heartily.

"I'll give you another jolly one," I said, and, replacing my whistle, I began with even greater zest to play "Yankee Doodle."

When I had gone through it half a dozen times with such added variations and trills as I could command, and had two of the children hopping about in the yard, and the forlorn man tapping his toe to the tune, and a smile on the face of the forlorn woman, I wound up with a rush, and then, as if I could hold myself in no longer (and I couldn't either!), I suddenly burst out:

> Yankee doodle dandy!
> Yankee doodle dandy!
> Mind the music and the step,
> And with the girls be handy.

It may seem surprising, but I think I can understand why it was — when I looked up at the woman in the doorway there were tears in her eyes!

"Do you know 'John Brown's Body'?" eagerly inquired the little girl with the dipper, and then, as if she had done something quite bold and improper, she blushed and edged toward the doorway.

"How does it go?" I asked, and one of the bold lads in the yard instantly puckered his lips to show me, and immediately they were all trying it.

"Here goes," said I, and for the next few minutes, and in my very best style, I hung Jeff Davis on the sour apple-tree, and I sent the soul of John Brown marching onward with an altogether unnecessary number of hallelujahs.

I think sometimes that people — whole families of 'em — literally perish for want of a good, hearty, whole-souled, mouth-opening, throat-stretching, side-aching laugh. They begin to think themselves the abused of creation, they begin to advise with their livers and to hate their neighbours, and the whole world becomes a miserable dark blue place quite unfit for human habitation. Well, all this is often only the result of a neglect to exercise properly those muscles of the body (and of the soul) which have to do with honest laughter.

I've never supposed I was an especially amusing person, but before I got through with it I had the Clark family well loosened up with laughter, although I wasn't quite sure some of the time whether Mrs. Clark was laughing or crying. I had them all laughing and talking, asking questions and answering them as though I were an old and valued neighbour.

Isn't it odd how unconvinced we often are by the crises in the lives of other people? They seem to us trivial or unimportant; but the fact is, the crises in the life of a boy, for example, or of a poor man, are as commanding as the crises in the life of the greatest statesman or millionaire, for they involve equally the whole personality, the entire prospects.

The Clark family, I soon learned, had lost its pig. A trivial matter, you say? I wonder if anything is ever trivial. A year of poor crops, sickness, low prices, discouragement — and, at the end of it, on top of it all, the cherished pig had died!

From all accounts (and the man on the porch quite lost his apathy in telling me about it) it must have been a pig of remarkable virtues and attainments, a paragon of pigs — in whom had been bound up the many possibilities of new shoes for the children, a hat for the lady, a new pair of overalls for the gentleman, and I know not what other kindred luxuries. I do not think, indeed, I ever had the portrait of a pig drawn for me with quite such ardent enthusiasm of detail, and the more questions I asked the more eager the story, until finally it became necessary for me to go to the barn, the cattle-pen, the pig-pen and the chicken-house, that I might visualize more clearly the scene of the tragedy. The whole family trooped after us like a classic chorus, but Mr. Clark himself kept the centre of the stage.

How plainly I could read upon the face of the land the story of this hill farmer and his meagre existence — his ill-directed effort to wring a poor living for his family from these upland fields, his poverty, and, above all, his evident lack of knowledge of his own calling. Added to these things, and perhaps the most depressing of all his difficulties, was the utter loneliness of the task, the feeling that it mattered little to any one whether the Clark family worked or not, or indeed whether they lived or died. A perfectly good American family was here being wasted, with the precious land they lived on, because no one had taken the trouble to make them feel that they were a part of this Great American Job.

As we went back to the house, a freckled-nosed neighbour's boy came in at the gate.

"A letter for you, Mr. Clark," said he. "I brought it up with our mail."

"A letter!" exclaimed Mrs. Clark.

"A letter!" echoed at least three of the children in unison.

"Probably a dun from Brewster," said Mr. Clark discouragingly.

I felt a curious sensation about the heart, and an eagerness of interest I have rarely experienced. I had no idea what a mere letter — a mere unopened unread letter — would mean to a family like this.

"It has no stamp on it!" exclaimed the older girl.

Mrs. Clark turned it over wonderingly in her hands. Mr. Clark hastily put on a pair of steel-bowed spectacles.

"Let me see it," he said, and when he also had inspected it minutely he solemnly tore open the envelope and drew forth my letter.

I assure you I never awaited the reading of any writing of mine with such breathless interest. How would they take it? Would they catch the meaning that I meant to convey? And would they suspect me of having written it?

Mr. Clark sat on the porch and read the letter slowly through to the end, turned the sheet over and examined it carefully, and then began reading it again to himself, Mrs. Clark leaning over his shoulder.

"What does it mean?" asked Mr. Clark.

"It's too good to be true," said Mrs. Clark with a sigh.

I don't know how long the discussion might have continued — probably for days or weeks — had not the older girl, now flushed of face and rather pretty, looked at me and said breathlessly (she was as sharp as a briar):

"You wrote it."

I stood the battery of all their eyes for a moment, smiling and rather excited.

"Yes," I said earnestly, "I wrote it, and I mean every word of it."

I had anticipated some shock of suspicion and inquiry, but to my surprise it was accepted as simply as a neighbourly good morning. I suppose the mystery of it was eclipsed by my astonishing presence there upon the scene with my tin whistle.

At any rate, it was a changed, eager, interested family which now occupied the porch of that dilapidated farmhouse. And immediately we fell into a lively discussion of crops and farming, and indeed the whole farm question, in which I found both the man and his wife singularly acute — sharpened upon the stone of hard experience.

Indeed, I found right here, as I have many times found among our American farmers, an intelligence (a literacy growing out of what I believe to be improper education) which was better able to discuss the problems of rural life than to grapple with and solve them. A dull, illiterate Polish farmer, I have found, will sometimes succeed much better at the job of life than his American neighbour.

Talk with almost any man for half an hour, and you will find that his conversation, like an old-fashioned song, has a regularly recurrent chorus. I soon discovered Mr. Clark's chorus.

"Now, if only I had a little cash," he sang, or, "If I had a few dollars, I could do so and so."

Why, he was as helplessly dependent upon money as any soft-handed millionairess. He considered himself poor and helpless because he lacked dollars, whereas people are really poor and helpless only when they lack courage and faith.

We were so much absorbed in our talk

that I was greatly surprised to hear Mrs. Clark's voice at the doorway.

"Won't you come in to supper?"

After we had eaten, there was a great demand for more of my tin whistle (oh, I know how Caruso must feel!), and I played over every blessed tune I knew, and some I didn't, four or five times, and after that we told stories and cracked jokes in a way that must have been utterly astonishing in that household. After the children had been, yes, driven to bed, Mr. Clark seemed about to drop back into his lamentations over his condition (which I have no doubt had come to give him a sort of pleasure), but I turned to Mrs. Clark, whom I had come to respect very highly, and began to talk about the little garden she had started, which was about the most enterprising thing about the place.

"Isn't it one of the finest things in this world," said I, "to go out into a good garden in the summer days and bring in loaded baskets filled with beets and cabbages and potatoes, just for the gathering?"

I knew from the expression on Mrs. Clark's face that I had touched a sounding note.

"Opening the green corn a little at the top to see if it is ready and then stripping it off and tearing away the moist white husks —— "

"And picking tomatoes?" said Mrs. Clark.

"And knuckling the watermelons to see if they are ripe? Oh, I tell you there are thousands of people in this country who'd like to be able to pick their dinner in the garden!"

"It's fine!" said Mrs. Clark with amused enthusiasm, "but I like best to hear the hens cackling in the barnyard in the morning after they've laid, and to go and bring in the eggs."

"Just like a daily present!" I said.

"Ye-es," responded the soundly practical Mrs. Clark, thinking, no doubt, that there were other aspects of the garden and chicken problem.

"I'll tell you another thing I like about a farmer's life," said I, "that's the smell in the house in the summer when there are preserves, or sweet pickles, or jam, or whatever it is, simmering on the stove. No matter where you are, up in the garret or down cellar, it's cinnamon, and allspice, and cloves, and every sort of sugary odour. Now, that gets me where I live!"

"It *is* good!" said Mrs. Clark with a laugh that could certainly be called nothing if not girlish.

All this time I had been keeping one eye on Mr. Clark. It was amusing to see him struggling against a cheerful view of life. He now broke into the conversation.

"Well, but ——" he began.

Instantly I headed him off.

"And think," said I, "of living a life in which you are beholden to no man. It's a free life, the farmer's life. No one can discharge you because you are sick, or tired, or old, or because you are a Democrat or a Baptist!"

"Well, but —— "

"And think of having to pay no rent, nor of having to live upstairs in a tenement!"

"Well, but ——"

"Or getting run over by a street-car, or having the children play in the gutters."

"I never did like to think of what my

children would do if we went to town," said Mrs. Clark.

"I guess not!" I exclaimed.

The fact is, most people don't think half enough of themselves and of their jobs; but before we went to bed that night I had the forlorn T. N. Clark talking about the virtues of his farm in quite a surprising way.

I even saw him eying me two or three times with a shrewd look in his eyes (your American is an irrepressible trader) as though I might possibly be some would-be purchaser in disguise.

(I shall write some time a dissertation on the advantages of wearing shabby clothing.)

The farm really had many good points. One of them was a shaggy old orchard of good and thriving but utterly neglected apple-trees.

"Man alive," I said, when we went out to see it in the morning, "you've got a gold mine here!" And I told him how in our neighbourhood we were renovating the old orchards, pruning them back, spraying, and bringing them into bearing again.

He had never, since he owned the place,

had a salable crop of fruit.   When we came
in to breakfast I quite stirred the practical
Mrs. Clark with my enthusiasm, and she
promised at once to send for a bulletin on
apple-tree renovation, published by the state
experiment station.   I am sure I was no
more earnest in my advice than the conditions
warranted.

After breakfast we went into the field,
and I suggested that instead of ploughing
any more land — for the season was already late — we get out all the accumulations of rotted manure from around the barn
and strew it on the land already ploughed
and harrow it in.

"A good job on a little piece of land,"
I said, "is far more profitable than a poor
job on a big piece of land."

Without more ado we got his old team
hitched up and began loading and haul-
ing out the manure, and spent all day long
at it.   Indeed, such was the height of enthusiasm which T. N. Clark now reached
(for his was a temperament that must either
soar in the clouds or grovel in the mire),
that he did not wish to stop when Mrs.
Clark called us in to supper.   In that one

day his crop of corn, in perspective, over-
flowed his crib, he could not find boxes and
barrels for his apples, his shed would not
hold all his tobacco, and his barn was already
being enlarged to accommodate a couple more
cows!   He was also keeping bees and growing
ginseng.

But it was fine, that evening, to see Mrs.
Clark's face, the renewed hope and courage
in it.   I thought as I looked at her (for she
was the strong and steady one in that
house):

"If you can keep the enthusiasm up,
if you can make that husband of yours
grow corn, and cows, and apples as you
raise chickens and make garden, there is
victory yet in this valley."

That night it rained, but in spite of the
moist earth we spent almost all of the following day hard at work in the field, and
all the time talking over ways and means
for the future, but the next morning, early,
I swung my bag on my back and left
them.

I shall not attempt to describe the friendliness of our parting. Mrs. Clark followed
me wistfully to the gate.

"I can't tell you ———" she began, with the tears starting in her eyes.

"Then don't try ———" said I, smiling.

And so I swung off down the country road, without looking back.

THE UNDISCOVERED COUNTRY

CHAPTER VII

THE UNDISCOVERED COUNTRY

IN SOME strange deep way there is no experience of my whole pilgrimage that I look back upon with so much wistful affection as I do upon the events of the day — the day and the wonderful night — which followed my long visit with the forlorn Clark family upon their hill farm. At first I hesitated about including an account of it here because it contains so little of what may be called thrilling or amusing incident.

"They want only the lively stories of my adventures," I said to myself, and I was at the point of pushing my notes to the edge of the table where (had I let go) they would have fallen into the convenient oblivion of the waste-basket. But something held me back.

"No," said I, "I'll tell it; if it meant so much to me, it may mean something to the friends who are following these lines."

For, after all, it is not what goes on outside of a man, the clash and clatter of superficial events, that arouses our deepest interest, but what goes on inside. Consider then that in this narrative I shall open a little door in my heart and let you look in, if you care to, upon the experiences of a day and a night in which I was supremely happy.

If you had chanced to be passing, that crisp spring morning, you would have seen a traveller on foot with a gray bag on his shoulder, swinging along the country road; and you might have been astonished to see him lift his hat at you and wish you a good morning. You might have turned to look back at him, as you passed, and found him turning also to look back at you — and wishing he might know you. But you would not have known what he was chanting under his breath as he tramped (how little we know of a man by the shabby coat he wears), nor how keenly he was enjoying the light airs and the warm sunshine of that fine spring morning.

After leaving the hill farm he had walked five miles up the valley, had crossed the ridge at a place called the Little Notch, where all the world lay stretched before him like the open palm of his hand, and had come thus to the boundaries of the Undiscovered Country. He had been for days troubled with the deep problems of other people, and it seemed to him this morning as though a great stone had been rolled from the door of his heart, and that he was entering upon a new world — a wonderful, high, free world. And, as he tramped, certain lines of a stanza long ago caught up in his memory from some forgotten page came up to his lips, and these were the words (you did not know as you passed) that he was chanting under his breath as he tramped, for they seem charged with the spirit of the hour:

> I've bartered my sheets for a starlit bed;
> I've traded my meat for a crust of bread;
> I've changed my book for a sapling cane,
> And I'm off to the end of the world again.

In the Undiscovered Country that morning it was wonderful how fresh the spring woods were, and how the birds sang in the trees, and how the brook sparkled and murmured at the roadside. The recent rain had washed the atmosphere until it was as clear and sparkling and heady as new wine, and the footing was firm and hard. As one tramped he could scarcely keep from singing or shouting aloud for the very joy of the day.

"I think," I said to myself, "I've never been in a better country," and it did not seem to me I cared to know where the gray road ran, nor how far away the blue hills were.

"It is wonderful enough anywhere here," I said.

And presently I turned from the road and climbed a gently sloping hillside among oak and chestnut trees. The earth was well carpeted for my feet, and here and there upon the hillside, where the sun came through the green roof of foliage, were warm splashes of yellow light, and here and there, on shadier slopes, the new ferns were spread upon the earth like some lacy coverlet. I finally sat down at the foot of a tree where through a rift in the foliage in the valley below I could catch a glimpse in the distance of the meadows and the misty blue hills. I was glad to rest, just rest, for the two previous days of hard labour, the labour and the tramping, had wearied me, and I sat for a long time quietly looking about me, scarcely thinking at all, but seeing, hearing, smelling — feeling the spring morning, and the woods, and the hills, and the patch of sky I could see.

For a long, long time I sat thus, but finally my mind began to flow again, and I thought how fine it would be if I had some good friend there with me to enjoy the perfect surroundings — some friend who would understand. And I thought of the Vedders with whom I had so recently spent a wonderful day; and I wished that they might be with me; there were so many things to be said — to be left unsaid. Upon this it occurred to me, suddenly, whimsically, and I exclaimed aloud:

"Why, I'll just call them up."

Half turning to the trunk of the tree where I sat, I placed one hand to my ear and the other to my lips and said:

"Hello, Central, give me Mr. Vedder."

I waited a moment, smiling a little at

my own absurdity and yet quite captivated by the enterprise.

"Is this Mr. Vedder? Oh, Mrs. Vedder! Well, this is David Grayson." . . .

"Yes, the very same. A bad penny, a rolling stone." . . .

"Yes. I want you both to come here as quickly as you can. I have the most important news for you. The mountain laurels are blooming, and the wild strawberries are setting their fruit. Yes, yes, and in the fields — all around here, to-day — there are wonderful white patches of daisies, and from where I sit I can see an old meadow as yellow as gold with buttercups. And the bobolinks are hovering over the low spots. Oh, but it is fine here — and we are not together!" . . .

"No; I cannot give exact directions. But take the Long Road and turn at the turning by the tulip-tree, and you will find me at home. Come right in without knocking."

I hung up the receiver. For a single instant it had seemed almost true, and indeed I believe — I wonder ——

Some day, I thought, just a bit sadly,

for I shall probably not be here then —
some day, we shall be able to call our friends
through space and time. Some day we
shall discover that marvellously simple coherer
by which we may better utilize the mysterious ether of love.

For a time I was sad with thoughts of
the unaccomplished future, and then I reflected that if I could not call up the Vedders
so informally I could at least write down a
few paragraphs which would give them some
faint impression of that time and place.
But I had no sooner taken out my note-book
and put down a sentence or two than I stuck
fast. How foolish and feeble written words
are anyway! With what glib facility they
describe, but how inadequately they convey.
A thousand times I have thought to myself,
"If only I could *write!*"

Not being able to write I turned, as I
have so often turned before, to some good
old book, trusting that I might find in the
writing of another man what I lacked in
my own. I took out my battered copy
of Montaigne and, opening it at random, as
I love to do, came, as luck would have it,
upon a chapter devoted to coaches, in which

there is much curious (and worthless) information, darkened with Latin quotations. This reading had an unexpected effect upon me.

I could not seem to keep my mind down upon the printed page; it kept bounding away at the sight of the distant hills, at the sound of a woodpecker on a dead stub which stood near me, and at the thousand and one faint rustlings, creepings, murmurings, tappings, which animate the mystery of the forest.   How dull indeed appeared the printed page in comparison with the book of life, how shut-in its atmosphere, how tinkling and distant the sound of its voices.   Suddenly I shut my book with a snap.

"Musty coaches and Latin quotations!" I exclaimed.   "Montaigne's no writer for the open air.   He belongs at a study fire on a quiet evening!"

I had anticipated, when I started out, many a pleasant hour by the roadside or in the woods with my books, but this was almost the first opportunity I had found for reading (as it was almost the last), so full was the present world of stirring events. As for poor old Montaigne, I have been out of harmony with him ever since, nor have I wanted him in the intimate case at my elbow.

After a long time in the forest, and the sun having reached the high heavens, I gathered up my pack and set forth again along the slope of the hills — not hurrying, just drifting and enjoying every sight and sound. And thus walking I came in sight, through the trees, of a glistening pool of water and made my way straight toward it.

A more charming spot I have rarely seen. In some former time an old mill had stood at the foot of the little valley, and a ruinous stone dam still held the water in a deep, quiet pond between two round hills. Above it a brook ran down through the woods, and below, with a pleasant musical sound, the water dripped over the mossy stone lips of the dam and fell into the rocky pool below. Nature had long ago healed the wounds of men; she had half covered the ruined mill with verdure, had softened the stone walls of the dam with mosses and lichens, and had crept down the steep hillside and was now leaning so far out over the pool that she could see her reflection in the quiet water.

Near the upper end of the pond I found a clear white sand-bank, where no doubt a thousand fishermen had stood, half hidden by the willows, to cast for trout in the pool below. I intended merely to drink and moisten my face, but as I knelt by the pool and saw my reflection in the clear water I wanted something more than that! In a moment I had thrown aside my bag and clothes and found myself wading naked into the water.

It was cold! I stood a moment there in the sunny air, the great world open around me, shuddering, for I dreaded the plunge — and then with a run, a shout and a splash I took the deep water. Oh, but it was fine! With long, deep strokes I carried myself fairly to the middle of the pond. The first chill was succeeded by a tingling glow, and I can convey no idea whatever of the glorious sense of exhilaration I had. I swam with the broad front stroke, I swam on my side, head half submerged, with a deep under stroke, and I rolled over on my back and swam with the water lapping my chin. Thus

I came to the end of the pool near the old dam, touched my feet on the bottom, gave a primeval whoop, and dove back into the water again. I have rarely experienced keener physical joy.   After swimming thus boisterously for a time, I quieted down to long, leisurely strokes, conscious of the water playing across my shoulders and singing at my ears, and finally, reaching the centre of the pond, I turned over on my back and, paddling lazily, watched the slow procession of light clouds across the sunlit openings of the trees above me. Away up in the sky I could see a hawk slowly swimming about (in his element as I was in mine), and nearer at hand, indeed fairly in the thicket about the pond, I could hear a wood-thrush singing.

And so, shaking the water out of my hair and swimming with long and leisurely strokes, I returned to the sand-bank, and there, standing in a spot of warm sunshine, I dried myself with the towel from my bag. And I said to myself:

"Surely it is good to be alive at a time like this!"

Slowly I drew on my clothes, idling there in the sand, and afterward I found an inviting spot in an old meadow where I threw myself down on the grass under an apple-tree and looked up into the shadowy places in the foliage above me. I felt a delicious sense of physical well-being, and I was pleasantly tired.

So I lay there — and the next thing I knew, I turned over, feeling cold and stiff, and opened my eyes upon the dusky shadows of late evening. I had been sleeping for hours!

The next few minutes (or was it an hour, or eternity?), I recall as containing some of the most exciting and, when all is said, amusing incidents in my whole life. And I got quite a new glimpse of that sometimes bumptious person known as David Grayson.

The first sensation I had was one of complete panic. What was I to do? Where was I to go?

Hastily seizing my bag — and before I was half awake — I started rapidly across the meadow, in my excitement tripping and falling several times in the first hundred yards. In daylight I have no doubt that I should easily have seen a gateway or at least an opening from the old meadow, but in the fast-gathering darkness it seemed to me that the open field was surrounded on every side by impenetrable forests. Absurd as it may seem, for no one knows what his mind will do at such a moment, I recalled vividly a passage from Stanley's story of his search for Livingstone, in which he relates how he escaped from a difficult place in the jungle by KEEPING STRAIGHT AHEAD.

I print these words in capitals because they seemed written that night upon the sky. *Keeping straight ahead*, I entered the forest on one side of the meadow (with quite a heroic sense of adventure), but scraped my shin on a fallen log and ran into a tree with bark on it that felt like a gigantic currycomb — and stopped!

Up to this point I think I was still partly asleep. Now, however, I waked up.

"All you need," said I to myself in my most matter-of-fact tone, "is a little cool sense. Be quiet now and reason it out."

So I stood there for some moments reasoning it out, with the result that I turned back and found the meadow again.

"What a fool I've been!" I said. "Isn't

it perfectly plain that I should have gone down to the pond, crossed over the inlet, and reached the road by the way I came?"

Having thus settled my problem, and congratulating myself on my perspicacity, I started straight for the mill-pond, but to my utter amazement, in the few short hours while I had been asleep, that entire body of water had evaporated, the dam had disappeared, and the stream had dried up. I must certainly present the facts in this remarkable case to some learned society.

I then decided to return to the old apple-tree where I had slept, which now seemed quite like home, but, strange to relate, the apple-tree had also completely vanished from the enchanted meadow. At that I began to suspect that in coming out of the forest I had somehow got into another and somewhat similar old field. I have never had a more confused or eerie sensation; not fear, but a sort of helplessness in which for an instant I actually began to doubt whether it was really I myself, David Grayson, who stood there in the dark meadow, or whether I was the victim of a peculiarly bad dream. I suppose many other people have had these sensations under similar conditions, but they were new to me.

I turned slowly around and looked for a light; I think I never wanted so much to see some sign of human habitation as I did at that moment.

What a coddled world we live in, truly. That being out after dark in a meadow should so disturb the very centre of our being! In all my life, indeed, and I suppose the same is true of ninty-nine out of a hundred of the people in America to-day, I had never before found myself where nothing stood between nature and me, where I had no place to sleep, no shelter for the night — nor any prospect of finding one. I was infinitely less resourceful at that moment than a rabbit, or a partridge, or a gray squirrel.

Presently I sat down on the ground where I had been standing, with a vague fear (absurd to look back upon!) that it, too, in some manner might slip away from under me. And as I sat there I began to have familiar gnawings at the pit of my stomach, and I remembered that, save for a couple of Mrs. Clark's dough-nuts eaten while I was sitting on the hillside, ages ago, I had had nothing since my early breakfast.

With this thought of my predicament — and the glimpse I had of myself "hungry and homeless" — the humour of the whole situation suddenly came over me, and, beginning with a chuckle, I wound up, as my mind dwelt upon my recent adventures, with a long, loud, hearty laugh.

As I laughed — and what a roar it made in that darkness! — I got up on my feet and looked up at the sky. One bright star shone out over the woods, and in the high heavens I could see dimly the white path of the Milky Way. And all at once I seemed again to be in command of myself and of the world. I felt a sudden lift and thrill of the spirits, a warm sense that this too was part of the great adventure — the Thing Itself.

"This is the light," I said looking up again at the sky and the single bright star, "which is set for me to-night. I will make my bed by it."

I can hope to make no one understand (unless he understands already) with what joy of adventure I now crept through the

meadow toward the wood. It was an un-
known, unexplored world I was in, and I,
the fortunate discoverer, had here to shift
for himself, make his home under the stars!
Marquette on the wild shores of the Mis-
sissippi, or Stanley in Africa, had no joy that
I did not know at that moment.

I crept along the meadow and came at
last to the wood. Here I chose a somewhat
sheltered spot at the foot of a large tree —
and yet a spot not so obscured that I could
not look out over the open spaces of the
meadow and see the sky. Here, groping in the
darkness, like some primitive creature, I raked
together a pile of leaves with my fingers,
and found dead twigs and branches of trees;
but in that moist forest (where the rain had
fallen only the day before) my efforts to
kindle a fire were unavailing. Upon this, I
considered using some pages from my note-
book, but another alternative suggested itself:

"Why not Montaigne?"

With that I groped for the familiar volume,
and with a curious sensation of satisfaction
I tore out a handful of pages from the back.

"Better Montaigne than Grayson," I said,
with a chuckle. It was amazing how Mon-

taigne sparkled and crackled when he was well lighted.

"There goes a bundle of quotations from Vergil," I said, "and there's his observations on the eating of fish. There are more uses than one for the classics."

So I ripped out a good part of another chapter, and thus, by coaxing, got my fire to going. It was not difficult after that to find enough fuel to make it blaze up warmly.

I opened my bag and took out the remnants of the luncheon which Mrs. Clark had given me that morning; and I was surprised and delighted to find, among the other things, a small bottle of coffee. This suggested all sorts of pleasing possibilities and, the spirit of invention being now awakened, I got out my tin cup, split a sapling stick so that I could fit it into the handle, and set the cup, full of coffee, on the coals at the edge of the fire. It was soon heated, and although I spilled some of it in getting it off, and although it was well spiced with ashes, I enjoyed it, with Mrs. Clark's doughnuts and sandwiches (some of which I toasted with a sapling fork) as thoroughly, I think, as ever I enjoyed any meal.

How little we know — we who dread life — how much there is in life!

My activities around the fire had warmed me to the bone, and after I was well through with my meal I gathered a plentiful supply of wood and placed it near at hand, I got out my waterproof cape and put it on, and, finally piling more sticks on the fire, I sat down comfortably at the foot of the tree.

I wish I could convey the mystery and the beauty of that night. Did you ever sit by a campfire and watch the flames dance, and the sparks fly upward into the cool dark air? Did you ever see the fitful light among the tree-depths, at one moment opening vast shadowy vistas into the forest, at the next dying downward and leaving it all in sombre mystery? It came to me that night with the wonderful vividness of a fresh experience.

And what a friendly and companionable thing a campfire is! How generous and outright it is! It plays for you when you wish to be lively, and it glows for you when you wish to be reflective.

After a while, for I did not feel in the

least sleepy, I stepped out of the woods to the edge of the pasture. All around me lay the dark and silent earth, and above the blue bowl of the sky, all glorious with the blaze of a million worlds. Sometimes I have been oppressed by this spectacle of utter space, of infinite distance, of forces too great for me to grasp or understand, but that night it came upon me with fresh wonder and power, and with a sense of great humility, that I belonged here too, that I was a part of it all — and would not be neglected or forgotten. It seemed to me I never had a moment of greater faith than that.

And so, with a sense of satisfaction and peace, I returned to my fire. As I sat there I could hear the curious noises of the woods, the little droppings, cracklings, rustlings which seemed to make all the world alive. I even fancied I could see small bright eyes looking out at my fire, and once or twice I was almost sure I heard voices — whispering — whispering — perhaps the voices of the woods.

Occasionally I added, with some amusement, a few dry pages of Montaigne to the fire, and watched the cheerful blaze that followed.

"No," said I, "Montaigne is not for the open spaces and the stars. Without a roof over his head Montaigne would — well, die of sneezing!"

So I sat all night long there by the tree. Occasionally I dropped into a light sleep, and then, as my fire died down, I grew chilly and awakened, to build up the fire and doze again. I saw the first faint gray streaks of dawn above the trees, I saw the pink glow in the east before the sunrise, and I watched the sun himself rise upon a new day ——

When I walked out into the meadow by daylight and looked about me curiously, I saw, not forty rods away, the back of a barn.

"Be you the fellow that was daown in my cowpastur' all night?" asked the sturdy farmer.

"I'm that fellow," I said.

"Why didn't you come right up to the house?"

"Well —— " I said, and then paused.

"Well . . ." said I.

THE HEDGE

CHAPTER VIII

THE HEDGE

STRANGE, strange, how small the big world is!

"Why didn't you come right into the house?" the sturdy farmer had asked me when I came out of the meadow where I had spent the night under the stars.

"Well," I said, turning the question as adroitly as I could, "I'll make it up by going into the house now."

So I went with him into his fine, comfortable house.

"This is my wife," said he.

A woman stood there facing me. "Oh!" she exclaimed, "Mr. Grayson!"

I recalled swiftly a child — a child she seemed then — with braids down her back, whom I had known when I first came to my farm. She had grown up, married, and had borne three children, while I had been looking the other way for a minute or two. She had not been in our neighbourhood for several years.

"And how is your sister and Doctor McAlway?"

Well, we had quite a wonderful visit, and she made breakfast for me, asking questions and talking eagerly as I ate.

"We've just had news that old Mr. Toombs is dead."

"Dead!" I exclaimed, dropping my fork; "old Nathan Toombs!"

"Yes, he was my uncle. Did you know him?"

"I knew Nathan Toombs," I said.

I spent two days there with the Ransomes, for they would not hear of my leaving, and half of our spare time, I think, was spent in discussing Nathan Toombs. I was not able to get him out of my mind for days, for his death was one of those events which prove so much and leave so much unproven.

I can recall vividly my astonishment at the first evidence I ever had of the strange old man or of his work. It was not very long after I came to my farm to live. I had taken to spending my spare evenings — the long evenings of summer — in exploring the country roads for miles around, getting acquainted with each farmstead, each bit of grove and meadow and marsh, making my best bow to each unfamiliar hill, and taking everywhere that toll of pleasure which comes of quiet discovery.

One evening, having walked farther than usual, I came quite suddenly around a turn in the road and saw stretching away before me an extraordinary sight.

I feel that I am conveying no adequate impression of what I beheld by giving it any such prim and decorous name as — a Hedge. It was a menagerie, a living, green menagerie! I had no sooner seen it than I began puzzling my brain as to whether one of the curious ornaments into which the upper part of the hedge had been clipped and trimmed was made to represent the head of a horse, or a camel, or an Egyptian sphinx.

The hedge was of arbor vitæ and as high as a man's waist. At more or less regular intervals the trees in it had been allowed to grow much taller and had been wonderfully pruned into the similitude of towers, pinnacles, bells, and many other strange designs. Here and there the hedge held up a spindling umbrella of greenery, sometimes a double umbrella — a little one above the big one — and over the gateway at the centre, as a sort of final triumph, rose a grandiose arch of interlaced branches upon which the artist had outdone himself in marvels of ornamentation.

I shall never forget the sensation of delight I had over this discovery, or of how I walked, tiptoe, along the road in front, studying each of the marvellous adornments. How eagerly, too, I looked over at the house beyond — a rather bare, bleak house set on a slight knoll or elevation and guarded at one corner by a dark spruce tree. At some distance behind I saw a number of huge barns, a cattle yard and a silo — all the evidences of prosperity — with well-nurtured fields, now yellowing with the summer crops, spreading pleasantly away on every hand.

It was nearly dark before I left that bit of roadside, and I shall never forget the eerie impression I had as I turned back to take a final look at the hedge, the strange, grotesque aspect it presented there in the half light with the bare, lonely house rising from the knoll behind.

It was not until some weeks later that I met the owner of the wonderful hedge. By that time, however, having learned of my interest, I found the whole countryside alive with stories about it and about Old Nathan Toombs, its owner. It was as though I had struck the rock of refreshment in a weary land.

I remember distinctly how puzzled I was by the stories I heard. The neighbourhood portrait — and ours is really a friendly neighbourhood — was by no means flattering. Old Toombs was apparently of that type of hard-shelled, grasping, self-reliant, old-fashioned farmer not unfamiliar to many country neighbourhoods. He had come of tough old American stock and he was a worker, a saver, and thus he had grown rich, the richest farmer in the whole neighbourhood. He was a regular individualistic American.

"A dour man," said the Scotch Preacher, "but just — you must admit that he is just."

There was no man living about whom the Scotch Preacher could not find something good to say.

"Yes, just," replied Horace, skeptically, "but hard — hard, and as mean as pusley."

This portrait was true enough in itself, for I knew just the sort of an aggressive, undoubtedly irritable old fellow it pictured, but somehow, try as I would, I could not see any such old fellow wasting his moneyed hours clipping bells, umbrellas, and camel's heads on his ornamental greenery. It left just that incongruity which is at once the lure, the humour, and the perplexity of human life. Instead of satisfying my curiosity I was more anxious than ever to see Old Toombs with my own eyes.

But the weeks passed and somehow I did not meet him. He was a lonely, unneighbourly old fellow. He had apparently come to fit into the community without ever really becoming a part of it. His neighbours accepted him as they accepted a hard hill in the town road. From time to time he would foreclose a mortgage where he had loaned money to some less thrifty farmer, or he would extend his acres by purchase, hard cash down, or he would build a bigger barn. When any of these things happened the community would crowd over a little, as it were, to give him more room. It is a curious thing, and tragic, too, when you come to think of it, how the world lets alone those people who appear to want to be let alone. "I can live to myself," says the unneighbourly one. "Well, live to yourself, then," cheerfully responds the world, and it goes about its more or less amusing affairs and lets the unneighbourly one cut himself off.

So our small community had let Old Toombs go his way with all his money, his acres, his hedge, and his reputation for being a just man.

Not meeting him, therefore, in the familiar and friendly life of the neighbourhood, I took to walking out toward his farm, looking freshly at the wonderful hedge and musing upon that most fascinating of all subjects — how men come to be what they are. And at last I was rewarded.

One day I had scarcely reached the end of the hedge when I saw Old Toombs himself moving toward me down the country road. Though I had never seen him before, I was at no loss to identify him. The first and vital impression he gave me, if I can compress it into a single word, was, I think, force — force. He came stubbing down the country road with a brown hickory stick in his hand, which at every step he set vigorously into the soft earth. Though not tall, he gave the impression of being enormously strong. He was thick, solid, firm — thick through the body, thick through the thighs; and his shoulders — what shoulders they were! — round like a maple log; and his great head with its thatching of coarse iron-gray hair, though thrust slightly forward, seemed set immovably upon them.

He presented such a forbidding appearance that I was of two minds about addressing him. Dour he was indeed! Nor shall I ever forget how he looked when I spoke to him. He stopped short there in the road. On his big square nose he wore a pair of curious spring-bowed glasses with black rims. For a moment he looked at me through these glasses, raising his chin a little, and then, deliberately wrinkling his nose, they fell off and dangled at the length of the faded cord by which they were hung. There was something almost uncanny about this peculiar habit of his and of the way in which, afterward, he looked at me from under his bushy gray brows. This was in truth the very man of the neighbourhood portrait.

"I am a new settler here," I said, "and I've been interested in looking at your wonderful hedge."

The old man's eyes rested upon me a moment with a mingled look of suspicion and hostility.

"So you've heard o' me," he said in a high-pitched voice, "and you've heard o' my hedge."

Again he paused and looked me over.

"Well," he said, with an indescribably harsh, cackling laugh, "I warrant you've heard nothing good o' me down there. I'm a skinflint, ain't I? I'm a hard citizen, ain't I? I grind the faces o' the poor, don't I?"

At first his words were marked by a sort of bitter humour, but as he continued to speak his voice rose higher and higher until it was positively menacing.

There were just two things I could do :— haul down the flag and retreat ingloriously,

or face the music. With a sudden sense of
rising spirits — for such things do not often
happen to a man in a quiet country road — I
paused a moment, looking him squarely in
the eye.

"Yes," I said, with great deliberation,
"you've given me just about the neighbourhood picture of yourself as I have had it.
They do say you are a skinflint, yes, and a
hard man. They say that you are rich and
friendless; they say that while you are a just
man, you do not know mercy. These are
terrible things to say of any man if they are
true."

I paused. The old man looked for a
moment as though he were going to strike
me with his stick, but he neither stirred
nor spoke. It was evidently a wholly new
experience for him.

"Yes," I said, "you are not popular in
this community, but what do you suppose
I care about that? I'm interested in your
hedge. What I'm curious to know — and I
might as well tell you frankly — is how such
a man as you are reputed to be could grow
such an extraordinary hedge. You must have
been at it a very long time."

I was surprised at the effect of my words. The old man turned partly aside and looked for a moment along the proud and flaunting embattlements of the green marvel before us. Then he said in a moderate voice:

"It's a putty good hedge, a putty good hedge."

"I've got him," I thought exultantly. "I've got him!"

"How long ago did you start it?" I pursued my advantage eagerly.

"Thirty-two years come spring," said he.

"Thirty-two years!" I repeated; "you've been at it a long time."

With that I plied him with questions in the liveliest manner, and in five minutes I had the gruff old fellow stumping along at my side and pointing out the various notable features of his wonderful creation. His suppressed excitement was quite wonderful to see. He would point his hickory stick with a poking motion, and, when he looked up, instead of throwing back his big, rough head, he bent at the hips, thus imparting an impression of astonishing solidity.

"It took me all o' ten years to get that bell right," he said, and, "Take a look at that arch: now what is your opinion o' that?"

Once, in the midst of our conversation, he checked himself abruptly and looked around at me with a sudden dark expression of suspicion. I saw exactly what lay in his mind, but I continued my questioning as though I perceived no change in him. It was only momentary, however, and he was soon as much interested as before. He talked as though he had not had such an opportunity before in years — and I doubt whether he had. It was plain to see that if any one ever loved anything in this world, Old Toombs loved that hedge of his. Think of it, indeed! He had lived with it, nurtured it, clipped it, groomed it — for thirty-two years.

So we walked down the sloping field within the hedge, and it seemed as though one of the deep mysteries of human nature was opening there before me. What strange things men set their hearts upon!

Thus, presently, we came nearly to the farther end of the hedge. Here the old man stopped and turned around, facing me.

"Do you see that valley?" he asked. "Do you see that slopin' valley up through my meadow?"

His voice rose suddenly to a sort of high-pitched violence.

"That passel o' hounds up there," he said, "want to build a road down my valley."

He drew his breath fiercely.

"They want to build a road through my land. They want to ruin my farm — they want to cut down my hedge. I'll fight 'em. I'll fight 'em. I'll show 'em yet!"

It was appalling. His face grew purple, his eyes narrowed to pin points and grew red and angry — like the eyes of an infuriated boar. His hands shook. Suddenly he turned upon me, poising his stick in his hand, and said violently.

"And who are you? Who are you? Are you one of these surveyor fellows?"

"My name," I answered as quietly as I could, "is Grayson. I live on the old Mather farm. I am not in the least interested in any of your road troubles."

He looked at me a moment more, and then seemed to shake himself or shudder, his eyes dropped away and he began walking toward his house. He had taken only a few steps, however, before he turned, and, without looking at me, asked if I would like to see the tools he used for trimming his hedge. When I hesitated, for I was decidedly uncomfortable, he came up to me and laid his hand awkwardly on my arm.

"You'll see something, I warrant, you never see before."

It was so evident that he regretted his outbreak that I followed him, and he showed me an odd double ladder set on low wheels which he said he used in trimming the higher parts of his hedge.

"It's my own invention," he said with pride.

"And that" — he pointed as we came out of the tool shed — "is my house — a good house. I planned it all myself. I never needed to take lessons of any carpenter I ever see. And there's my barns. What do you think 'o' my barns? Ever see any bigger ones? They ain't any bigger in this country than Old Toombs's barns. They don't like Old Toombs, but they ain't any of 'em can ekal his barns!"

" ' I'll fight 'em, I'll show 'em yet!' "

He followed me down to the roadside now quite loquacious. Even after I had thanked him and started to go he called after me. When I stopped he came forward hesitatingly — and I had the impressions, suddenly, and for the first time that he was an old man. It may have been the result of his sudden fierce explosion of anger, but his hand shook, his face was pale, and he seemed somehow broken.

"You — you like my hedge?" he asked.

"It is certainly a wonderful hedge," I said. "I never have seen anything like it."

"The' *ain't* nothing like it," he responded, quickly. "The' ain't nothing like it anywhere."

In the twilight as I passed onward I saw the lonely figure of the old man moving with his hickory stick up the pathway to his lonely house. The poor rich old man!

"He thinks he can live wholly to himself," I said aloud.

I thought, as I tramped homeward, of our friendly and kindly community, of how we often come together of an evening with skylarking and laughter, of how we weep with one another, of how we join in making better roads and better schools, and in building up the Scotch Preacher's friendly little church.   And in all these things Old Toombs has never had a part.   He is not even missed.

As a matter of fact, I reflected, and this is a strange, deep thing, no man is in reality more dependent upon the community which he despises and holds at arm's length than this same Old Nathan Toombs.   Everything he has, everything he does, gives evidence of it.   And I don't mean this in any mere material sense, though of course his wealth and his farm would mean no more than the stones in his hills to him if he did not have us here around him.   Without our work, our buying, our selling, our governing, his dollars would be dust.   But we are still more necessary to him in other ways: the unfriendly man is usually the one who demands most from his neighbours.   Thus, if he have not people's love or confidence, then he will smite them until they fear him, or admire him, or hate him.   Oh, no man, however he may try, can hold himself aloof!

I came home deeply stirred from my visit with Old Toombs and lost no time in making further inquiries. I learned, speedily, that there was indeed something in the old man's dread of a road being built through his farm. The case was already in the courts. His farm was a very old one and extensive, and of recent years a large settlement of small farmers had been developing the rougher lands in the upper part of the township, called the Swan Hill district. Their only way to reach the railroad was by a rocky, winding road among the hills, while their natural outlet was down a gently sloping valley through Old Toombs's farm. They were now so numerous and politically important that they had stirred up the town authorites. A proposition had been made to Old Toombs for a right-of-way; they argued with him that it was a good thing for the whole country, that it would enhance the values of his own upper lands, and that they would pay him far more for a right-of-way than the land was actually worth, but he had spurned them — I can imagine with what vehemence.

"Let 'em drive round," he said. "Didn't they know what they'd hev to do when they settled up there? What a passel o' curs!

They can keep off o' my land, or I'll have the law on 'em."

And thus the matter came to the courts with the town attempting to condemn the land for a road through Old Toombs's farm.

"What can we do?" asked the Scotch Preacher, who was deeply distressed by the bitterness of feeling displayed. "There is no getting to the man. He will listen to no one."

At one time I thought of going over and talking with Old Toombs myself, for it seemed that I had been able to get nearer to him than any one had in a long time. But I dreaded it. I kept dallying — for what, indeed, could I have said to him? If he had been suspicious of me before, how much more hostile he might be when I expressed an interest in his difficulties. As to reaching the Swan Hill settlers, they were now aroused to an implacable state of bitterness; and they had the people of the whole community with them, for no one liked Old Toombs.

Thus while I hesitated time passed and my next meeting with Old Toombs, instead of being premediated, came about quite unexpectedly. I was walking in the town road late one afternoon when I heard a wagon rattling behind me, and then, quite suddenly, a shouted, "Whoa!"

Looking around, I saw Old Toombs, his great solid figure mounted high on the wagon seat, the reins held fast in the fingers of one hand. I was struck by the strange expression in his face — a sort of grim exaltation. As I stepped aside he burst out in a loud, shrill, cackling laugh:

"He-he-he — he-he-he —— "

I was too astonished to speak at once. Ordinarily when I meet any one in the town road it is in my heart to cry out to him, "Good morning, friend," or, "How are you, brother?" but I had no such prompting that day.

"Git in, Grayson," he said; "git in, git in."

I climbed up beside him, and he slapped me on the knee with another burst of shrill laughter.

"They thought they had the old man," he said, starting up his horses. "They thought there weren't no law left in Israel. I showed 'em."

I cannot convey the bitter triumphancy of his voice.

"You mean the road case?" I asked.

"Road case!" he exploded, "they wan't no road case; they didn't have no road case. I beat 'em. I says to 'em, 'What right hev any o' you on my property? Go round with you,' I says. Oh, I beat 'em. If they'd had their way, they'd 'a' cut through my hedge — the hounds!"

When he set me down at my door I had said hardly a word. There seemed nothing that could be said. I remember I stood for some time watching the old man as he rode away, his wagon jolting in the country road, his stout figure perched firmly in the seat. I went in with a sense of heaviness at the heart.

"Harriet," I said, "there are some things in this world beyond human remedy."

Two evenings later I was surprised to see the Scotch Preacher drive up to my gate and hastily tie his horse.

"David," said he, "there's bad business afoot. A lot of the young fellows in Swan Hill are planning a raid on Old Toombs's hedge. They are coming down to-night."

I got my hat and jumped in with him. We drove up the hilly road and out around Old Toombs's farm and thus came, near sundown, to the settlement. I had no conception of the bitterness that the lawsuit had engendered.

"Where once you start men hating one another," said the Scotch Preacher, "there's utterly no end of it."

I have seen our Scotch Preacher in many difficult places, but never have I seen him rise to greater heights than he did that night. It is not in his preaching that Doctor Mc-Alway excels, but what a power he is among men! He was like some stern old giant, standing there and holding up the portals of civilization. I saw men melt under his words like wax; I saw wild young fellows subdued into quietude; I saw unwise old men set to thinking.

"Man, man," he'd say, lapsing in his earnestness into the broad Scotch accent of his youth, "you canna' mean plunder, and destruction, and riot! You canna! Not in this neighbourhood!"

"What about Old Toombs?" shouted one of the boys.

I never shall forget how Doctor McAlway drew himself up, nor the majesty that looked from his eye.

"Old Toombs!" he said in a voice that thrilled one to the bone, "Old Toombs! Have you no faith, that you stand in the place of Almighty God and measure punishments?"

Before we left it was past midnight and we drove home, almost silent, in the darkness.

"Doctor McAlway," I said, "if Old Toombs could know the history of this night it might change his point of view."

"I doot it," said the Scotch Preacher. "I doot it."

The night passed serenely; the morning saw Old Toombs's hedge standing as gorgeous as ever. The community had again stepped aside and let Old Toombs have his way: they had let him alone, with all his great barns, his wide acres and his wonderful hedge. He probably never even knew what had threatened him that night, nor how the forces of religion, of social order, of neighbourliness in the community which he despised had, after all, held him safe. There is a supreme faith among common people — it is, indeed, the very taproot of democracy — that although the unfriendly one may persist long in his power and arrogance, there is a moving Force which commands events.

I suppose if I were writing a mere story I should tell how Old Toombs was miraculously softened at the age of sixty-eight years, and came into new relationships with his neighbours, or else I should relate how the mills of God, grinding slowly, had crushed the recalcitrant human atom into dust.

Either of these results conceivably might have happened — all things are possible — and being ingeniously related would somehow have answered a need in the human soul that the logic of events be constantly and conclusively demonstrated in the lives of individual men and women.

But as a matter of fact, neither of these things did happen in this quiet community of ours. There exists, assuredly, a logic of events, oh, a terrible, irresistible logic of events, but it is careless of the span of any one man's life. We would like to have each man enjoy the sweets of his own virtues and suffer the lash of his own misdeeds — but it rarely so happens in life. No, it is the community which lives or dies, is regenerated or marred by the deeds of men.

So Old Toombs continued to live. So he continued to buy more land, raise more cattle, collect more interest, and the wonderful hedge continued to flaunt its marvels still more notably upon the country road. To what end? Who knows? Who knows?

I saw him afterward from time to time, tried to maintain some sort of friendly relations with him; but it seemed as the years passed that he grew ever lonelier and more bitter, and not only more friendless, but seemingly more incapable of friendliness. In times past I have seen what men call tragedies — I saw once a perfect young man die in his strength — but it seems to me I never knew anything more tragic than the life and death of Old Toombs. If it cannot be said of a man when he dies that either his nation, his state, his neighbourhood, his family, or at least his wife or child, is better for his having lived, what *can* be said for him?

Old Toombs is dead. Like Jehoram, King of Judah, of whom it is terribly said in the Book of Chronicles, "he departed without being desired."

Of this story of Nathan Toombs we talked much and long there in the Ransome home. I was with them, as I said, about two days — kept inside most of the time by a driving spring rain which filled the valley with a pale gray mist and turned all the country roads into running streams. One morning, the weather having cleared, I swung my bag to my shoulder, and with much warmth of parting I set my face again to the free road and the open country.

THE MAN POSSESSED

CHAPTER IX

THE MAN POSSESSED

I SUPPOSE I was predestined (and like-wise foreordained) to reach the city sooner or later. My fate in that respect was settled for me when I placed my trust in the vagrant road. I thought for a time that I was more than a match for the Road, but I soon learned that the Road was more than a match for me. Sly? There's no name for it. Alluring, lovable, mysterious — as the heart of a woman. Many a time I've followed the Road where it led through innocent meadows or climbed leisurely hill slopes only to find that it had crept around slyly and led me before I knew it into the back door of some busy town.

Mostly in this country the towns squat low in the valleys, they lie in wait by the rivers, and often I scarcely know of their presence until I am so close upon them that I can smell the breath of their heated nostrils and hear their low growlings and grumblings.

My fear of these lesser towns has never been profound. I have even been bold enough, when I came across one of them, to hasten straight through as though assured that Cerberus was securely chained; but I found, after a time, what I might indeed have guessed, that the Road also led irresistibly to the lair of the Old Monster himself, the He-one of the species, where he lies upon the plain, lolling under his soiled gray blanket of smoke.

It is wonderful to be safe at home again, to watch the tender, reddish brown shoots of the Virginia creeper reaching in at my study window, to see the green of my own quiet fields, to hear the peaceful clucking of the hens in the sunny dooryard — and Harriet humming at her work in the kitchen.

When I left the Ransomes that fine spring morning, I had not the slightest presentiment of what the world held in store for me. After being a prisoner of the weather for so long, I took to the Road with fresh joy. All the fields were of a misty greenness and there were pools still shining in the road, but the air was deliciously clear, clean, and soft. I came through the hill country for three or four miles, even running down some of the steeper places for the very joy the motion gave me, the feel of the air on my face.

Thus I came finally to the Great Road, and stood for a moment looking first this way, then that.

"Where now?" I asked aloud.

With an amusing sense of the possibilities that lay open before me, I closed my eyes, turned slowly around several times and then stopped. When I opened my eyes I was facing nearly southward: and that way I set out, not knowing in the least what

Fortune had presided at that turning.   If I
had gone the other way ——

I walked vigorously for two or three
hours, meeting or passing many interesting
people upon the busy road.   Automobiles
there were in plenty, and loaded wagons, and
jolly families off for town, and a herdsman
driving sheep, and small boys on their way to
school with their dinner pails, and a gypsy
wagon with lean, led horses following behind,
and even a Jewish peddler with a crinkly
black beard, whom I was on the very point
of stopping.

"I should like sometime to know a Jew,"
I said to myself.

As I travelled, feeling like one who pos-
sesses hidden riches, I came quite without
warning upon the beginning of my great
adventure.   I had been looking for a certain
thing all the morning, first on one side of
the road, then the other, and finally I was
rewarded.   There it was, nailed high upon a
tree, the curious, familiar sign:

```
┌─────────────────────────┐
│                         │
│          REST           │
│                         │
└─────────────────────────┘
```

I stopped instantly.   It seemed like an old friend.

"Well," said I.   "I'm not at all tired, but I want to be agreeable."

With that I sat down on a convenient stone, took off my hat, wiped my forehead, and looked about me with satisfaction, for it was a pleasant country.

I had not been sitting there above two minutes when my eyes fell upon one of the oddest specimens of humanity (I thought then) that ever I saw.   He had been standing near the roadside, just under the tree upon which I had seen the sign, "Rest."   My heart dotted and carried one.

"The sign man himself!" I exclaimed.

I arose instantly and walked down the road toward him.

"A man has only to stop anywhere here," I said exultantly, "and things happen."

The stranger's appearance was indeed extraordinary.   He seemed at first glimpse to be about twice as large around the hips as he was at the shoulders, but this I soon discovered to be due to no natural avoirdupois but to the prodigious number of soiled newspapers and magazines with which the low-hanging pockets of his overcoat were stuffed. For he was still wearing an old shabby overcoat — though the weather was warm and bright — and on his head was an odd and outlandish hat. It was of fur, flat at the top, flat as a pie tin, with the moth-eaten earlaps turned up at the sides and looking exactly like small furry ears. These, with the round steel spectacles which he wore — the only distinctive feature of his countenance — gave him an indescribably droll appearance.

"A fox!" I thought.

Then I looked at him more closely.

"No," said I, "an owl, an owl!"

The stranger stepped out into the road and evidently awaited my approach. My first vivid impression of his face — I remember it afterward shining with a strange inward illumination — was not favourable. It was a deep-lined, scarred, worn-looking face, insignificant if not indeed ugly in its features, and yet, even at the first glance, revealing something inexplainable — incalculable ——

"Good day, friend," I said heartily.

Without replying to my greeting, he asked:

"Is this the road to Kilburn?" — with a faint flavour of foreignness in his words.

"I think it is," I replied, and I noticed as he lifted his hand to thank me that one finger was missing and that the hand itself was cruelly twisted and scarred.

The stranger instantly set off up the Road without giving me much more attention than he would have given any other sign-post. I stood a moment looking after him — the wings of his overcoat beating about his legs and the small furry ears on his cap wagging gently.

"There," said I aloud, "is a man who is actually going somewhere."

So many men in this world are going nowhere in particular that when one comes along — even though he be amusing and insignificant — who is really (and passionately) going somewhere, what a stir he communicates to a dull world! We catch sparks of electricity from the very friction of his passage.

It was so with this odd stranger. Though at one moment I could not help smiling at him, at the next I was following him.

"It may be," said I to myself, "that this is really the sign man!"

I felt like Captain Kidd under full sail to capture a treasure ship; and as I approached, I was much agitated as to the best method of grappling and boarding. I finally decided, being a lover of bold methods, to let go my largest gun first — for moral effect.

"So," said I, as I ran alongside, "you are the man who puts up the signs."

He stopped and looked at me.

"What signs?"

"Why the sign 'Rest' along this road."

He paused for some seconds with a perplexed expression on his face.

"Then you are not the sign man," I said.

"No," he replied, "I ain't any sign man."

I was not a little disappointed, but having made my attack, I determined to see if there was any treasure aboard — which, I suppose, should be the procedure of any well-regulated pirate.

"I'm going this way myself," I said, "and if you have no objections ——"

He stood looking at me curiously, indeed suspiciously, through his round spectacles.

"Have you got the passport?" he asked finally.

" ' *So you are the man who puts up the signs* ' "

"The passport!" I exclaimed, mystified in my turn.

"Yes," said he, "the passport. Let me see your hand."

When I held out my hand he looked at it closely for a moment, and then took it with a quick warm pressure in one of his, and gave it a little shake, in a way not quite American.

"You are one of us," said he, "you work."

I thought at first that it was a bit of pleasantry, and I was about to return it in kind when I saw plainly in his face a look of solemn intent.

"So," he said, "we shall travel like comrades."

He thrust his scarred hand through my arm, and we walked up the road side by side, his bulging pockets beating first against his legs and then against mine, quite impartially.

"I think," said the stranger, "that we shall be arrested at Kilburn."

"We shall!" I exclaimed with something, I admit, of a shock.

"Yes," he said, "but it is all in the day's work."

"How is that?"

He stopped in the road and faced me. Throwing back his overcoat he pointed to a small red button on his coat lapel.

"They don't want me in Kilburn," said he, "the mill men are strikin' there, and the bosses have got armed men on every corner. Oh, the capitalists are watchin' for me, all right."

I cannot convey the strange excitement I felt. It seemed as though these words suddenly opened a whole new world around me — a world I had heard about for years, but never entered. And the tone in which he had used the word "capitalist!" I had almost to glance around to make sure that there were no ravening capitalists hiding behind the trees.

"So you are a Socialist," I said.

"Yes," he answered. "I'm one of those dangerous persons."

First and last I have read much of Socialism, and thought about it, too, from the quiet angle of my farm among the hills, but this was the first time I had ever had a live Socialist on my arm. I could not have been more surprised if the stranger had said, "Yes, I am Theodore Roosevelt."

One of the discoveries we keep making all our life long (provided we remain humble) is the humorous discovery of the ordinariness of the extraordinary. Here was this disrupter of society, this man of the red flag — here he was with his mild spectacled eyes and his furry ears wagging as he walked. It was unbelievable! — and the sun shining on him quite as impartially as it shone on me.

Coming at last to a pleasant bit of woodland, where a stream ran under the roadway, I said:

"Stranger, let's sit down and have a bite of luncheon."

He began to expostulate, said he was expected in Kilburn.

"Oh, I've plenty for two," I said, "and I can say, at least, that I am a firm believer in coöperation."

Without more urging he followed me into the woods, where we sat down comfortably under a tree.

Now, when I take a fine thick sandwich out of my bag, I always feel like making it a polite bow, and before I bite into a big brown doughnut, I am tempted to say, "By your leave, madam," and as for MINCE

PIE — Beau Brummel himself could not outdo me in respectful consideration. But Bill Hahn neither saw, nor smelled, nor, I think, tasted Mrs. Ransome's cookery. As soon as we sat down he began talking. From time to time he would reach out for another sandwich or doughnut or pickle (without knowing in the least which he was getting), and when that was gone some reflex impulse caused him to reach out for some more. When the last crumb of our luncheon had disappeared Bill Hahn still reached out. His hand groped absently about, and coming in contact with no more doughnuts or pickles he withdrew it — and did not know, I think, that the meal was finished. (Confidentially, I have speculated on what might have happened if the supply had been unlimited!)

But that was Bill Hahn. Once started on his talk, he never thought of food or clothing or shelter; but his eyes glowed, his face lighted up with a strange effulgence, and he quite lost himself upon the tide of his own oratory. I saw him afterward by a flare-light at the centre of a great crowd of men and women — but that is getting ahead of my story.

His talk bristled with such words as "capitalism," "proletariat," "class-conscious-ness" — and he spoke with fluency of "economic determinism" and "syndicalism." It was quite wonderful! And from time to time, he would bring in a smashing quotation from Aristotle, Napoleon, Karl Marx, or Eugene V. Debs, giving them all equal values, and he cited statistics! — oh, marvellous statistics, that never were on sea or land.

Once he was so swept away by his own eloquence that he sprang to his feet and, raising one hand high above his head (quite unconscious that he was holding up a dill pickle), he worked through one of his most thrilling periods.

Yes, I laughed, and yet there was so brave a simplicity about this odd, absurd little man that what I laughed at was only his outward appearance (and that he himself had no care for), and all the time I felt a growing respect and admiration for him. He was not only sincere, but he was genuinely simple—a much higher virtue, as Fenelon says. For while sincere people do not aim at appearing anything but what they are, they are always in fear of passing for something they are not. They are forever thinking about themselves, weighing all their words and thoughts and dwelling upon what they have done, in the fear of having done too much or too little, whereas simplicity, as Fenelon says, is an uprightness of soul which has ceased wholly to dwell upon itself or its actions. Thus there are plenty of sincere folk in the world but few who are simple.

Well, the longer he talked, the less interested I was in what he said and the more fascinated I became in what he was. I felt a wistful interest in him: and I wanted to know what way he took to purge himself of himself. I think if I had been in that group, nineteen hundred years ago, which surrounded the beggar who was born blind, but whose anointed eyes now looked out upon the glories of the world, I should have been among the questioners:

"What did he to thee? How opened he thine eyes?"

I tried ineffectually several times to break the swift current of his oratory and finally succeeded (when he paused a moment to finish off a bit of pie crust).

"You must have seen some hard experiences in your life," I said.

"That I have," responded Bill Hahn, "the capitalistic system ——"

"Did you ever work in the mills yourself?" I interrupted hastily.

"Boy and man," said Bill Hahn, "I worked in that hell for thirty-two years — The class-conscious proletariat have only to exert themselves —— "

"And your wife, did she work too — and your sons and daughters?"

A spasm of pain crossed his face.

"My daughter?" he said. "They killed her in the mills."

It was appalling — the dead level of the tone in which he uttered those words — the monotone of an emotion long ago burned out, and yet leaving frightful scars.

"My friend!" I exclaimed, and I could not help laying my hand on his arm.

I had the feeling I often have with troubled children—an indescribable pity that they have had to pass through the valley of the shadow, and I not there to take them by the hand.

"And was this — your daughter — what brought you to your present belief?"

"No," said he, "oh, no.   I was a Socialist, as you might say, from youth up. That is, I called myself a Socialist, but, comrade, I've learned this here truth: that it ain't of so much importance that you possess a belief, as that the belief possess you. Do you understand?"

"I think," said I, "that I understand."

Well, he told me his story, mostly in a curious, dull, detached way — as though he were speaking of some third person in whom he felt only a brotherly interest, but from time to time some incident or observation would flame up out of the narrative, like the opening of the door of a molten pit — so that the glare hurt one! — and then the story would die back again into quiet narrative.

Like most working people he had never lived in the twentieth century at all.   He was still in the feudal age, and his whole life had been a blind and ceaseless struggle for the bare necessaries of life, broken from time to time by fierce irregular wars called strikes. He had never known anything of a real self-governing commonwealth, and such progress as he and his kind had made was never the result of their citizenship, of their powers as voters, but grew out of the explosive and ragged upheavals of their own half-organized societies and unions.

It was against the "black people" he said that he was first on strike back in the early nineties. He told me all about it, how he had been working in the mills pretty comfortably — he was young and strong then, with a fine growing family and a small home of his own.

"It was as pretty a place as you would want to see," he said; "we grew cabbages and onions and turnips — everything grew fine! — in the garden behind the house."

And then the "black people" began to come in, little by little at first, and then by the carload. By the "black people" he meant the people from Southern Europe, he called them "hordes" — "hordes and hordes of 'em" — Italians mostly, and they began getting into the mills and underbidding for the jobs, so that wages slowly went down and at the same time the machines were speeded up. It seems that many of these "black people" were single men or vigorous young married people with only themselves to support, while the old American workers were men

with families and little homes to pay for,
and plenty of old grandfathers and grand-
mothers, to say nothing of babies, depending
upon them.

"There wasn't a living for a decent family
left," he said.

So they struck — and he told me in his
dull monotone of the long bitterness of that
strike, the empty cupboards, the approach
of winter with no coal for the stoves and no
warm clothing for the children. He told
me that many of the old workers began to
leave the town (some bound for the larger
cities, some for the Far West).

"But," said he with a sudden outburst
of emotion, "I couldn't leave. I had the
woman and the children!"

And presently the strike collapsed, and
the workers rushed helter skelter back to the
mills to get their old jobs. "Begging like
whipped dogs," he said bitterly.

Many of them found their places taken
by the eager "black people," and many had
to go to work at lower wages in poorer places
— punished for the fight they had made.

But he got along somehow, he said —
'the woman was a good manager" — until

one day he had the misfortune to get his hand caught in the machinery. It was a place which should have been protected with guards, but was not. He was laid up for several weeks, and the company, claiming that the accident was due to his own stupidity and carelessness, refused even to pay his wages while he was idle. Well, the family had to live somehow, and the woman and the daughter — "she was a little thing," he said, "and frail" — the woman and the daughter went into the mill. But even with this new source of income they began to fall behind. Money which should have gone toward making the last payments on their home (already long delayed by the strike) had now to go to the doctor and the grocer.

"We had to live," said Bill Hahn.

Again and again he used this same phrase, "We had to live!" as a sort of bedrock explanation for all the woes of life.

After a time, with one finger gone and a frightfully scarred hand — he held it up for me to see — he went back into the mill.

"But it kept getting worse and worse," said he, "and finally I couldn't stand it any longer."

He and a group of friends got together secretly and tried to organize a union, tried to get the workmen together to improve their own condition; but in some way ("they had spies everywhere," he said) the manager learned of the attempt and one morning when he reported at the mill he was handed a slip asking him to call for his wages, that his help was no longer required.

"I'd been with that one company for twenty years and four months," he said bitterly, "I'd helped in my small way to build it up, make it a big concern payin' 28 per cent. dividends every year; I'd given part of my right hand in doin' it — and they threw me out like an old shoe."

He said he would have pulled up and gone away, but he still had the little home and the garden, and his wife and daughter were still at work, so he hung on grimly, trying to get some other job. "But what good is a man for any other sort of work," he said, "when he has been trained to the mills for thirty-two years!"

It was not very long after that when the "great strike" began — indeed, it grew out of the organization which he had tried to launch — and Bill Hahn threw himself into it with all his strength. He was one of the leaders. I shall not attempt to repeat here his description of the bitter struggle, the coming of the soldiery, the street riots, the long lists of arrests ("some," said he, "got into jail on purpose, so that they could at least have enough to eat!"), the late meetings of strikers, the wild turmoil and excitement.

Of all this he told me, and then he stopped suddenly, and after a long pause he said in a low voice:

"Comrade, did ye ever see your wife and your sickly daughter and your kids sufferin' for bread to eat?"

He paused again with a hard, dry sob in his voice.

"Did ye ever see that?"

"No," said I, very humbly, "I have never seen anything like that."

He turned on me suddenly, and I shall never forget the look on his face, nor the blaze in his eyes:

"Then what can you know about working-men!"

What could I answer?

A moment passed and then he said, as if a

little remorseful at having turned thus upon me:

"Comrade, I tell you, the iron entered my soul — them days."

It seems that the leaders of the strike were mostly old employees like Bill Hahn, and the company had conceived the idea that if these men could be eliminated the organization would collapse, and the strikers be forced back to work. One day Bill Hahn found that proceedings had been started to turn him out of his home, upon which he had not been able to keep up his payments, and at the same time the merchant, of whom he had been a respected customer for years, refused to give him any further credit.

"But we lived somehow," he said, "we lived and we fought."

It was then that he began to see clearly what it all meant. He said he made a great discovery: that the "black people" against whom they had struck in 1894 were not to blame!

"I tell you," said he, "we found when we got started that them black people — we used to call 'em dagoes — were just workin' people like us — and in hell with us. They were good soldiers, them Eyetalians and Poles and Syrians, they fought with us to the end."

I shall not soon forget the intensely dramatic but perfectly simple way in which he told me how he came, as he said, "to see the true light." Holding up his maimed right hand (that trembled a little), he pointed one finger upward.

"I seen the big hand in the sky," he said, "I seen it as clear as daylight."

He said he saw at last what Socialism meant.

One day he went home from a strikers' meeting — one of the last, for the men were worn out with their long struggle. It was a bitter cold day, and he was completely discouraged. When he reached his own street he saw a pile of household goods on the side-walk in front of his home. He saw his wife there wringing her hands and crying. He said he could not take a step further, but sat down on a neighbour's porch and looked and looked. "It was curious," he said, "but the only thing I could see or think about was our old family clock which they had stuck on top of the pile, half tipped over. It looked odd and I wanted to set it up straight. It was the clock we bought when we were

married, and we'd had it about twenty years
on the mantel in the livin'-room.   It was a
good clock," he said.

He paused and then smiled a little.

"I never have figured it out why I should
have been able to think of nothing but that
clock," he said, "but so it was."

When he got home, he found his frail
daughter just coming out of the empty house,
"coughing as though she was dyin'."   Something, he said, seemed to stop inside of him.
Those were his words: "Something seemed
to stop inside 'o me."

He turned away without saying a word,
walked back to strike headquarters, bor-
rowed a revolver from a friend, and started
out along the main road which led into the
better part of the town.

"Did you ever hear o' Robert Winter?"
he asked.

"No," said I.

"Well, Robert Winter was the biggest
gun of 'em all.   He owned the mills there,
and the largest store and the newspaper —
he pretty nearly owned the town."

He told me much more about Robert
Winter which betrayed still a curious sort

of feudal admiration for him, and for his great place and power; but I need not dwell on it here.   He told me how he climbed in through a hemlock hedge (for the stone gateway was guarded) and walked through the snow toward the great house.

"An' all the time I seemed to be seein' my daughter Margy right there before my eyes coughing as though she was dyin'."

It was just nightfall and all the windows were alight.   He crept up to a clump of bushes under a window and waited there a moment while he drew out and cocked his revolver.   Then he slowly reached upward until his head cleared the sill and he could look into the room.   "A big, warm room," he described it.

"Comrade," said he, "I had murder in my heart that night."

So he stood there looking in with the revolver ready cocked in his hand.

"And what do you think I seen there?" he asked.

"I cannot guess," I said.

"Well," said Bill Hahn, "I seen the great Robert Winter that we had been fighting for five long months—and he was down on his hands and knees on the carpet — and he had his little daughter on his back — and he was creepin' about with her — an' she was laughin'."

Bill Hahn paused.

"I had a bead on him," he said finally, "but I couldn't do it — I just couldn't do it."

He came away all weak and trembling and cold, and, "Comrade," he said, "I was cryin' like a baby, and didn't know why."

The next day the strike collapsed and there was the familiar stampede for work — but Bill Hahn did not go back. He knew it would be useless. A week later his frail daughter died and was buried in the pauper's field.

"She was as truly killed," he said, "as though some one had fired a bullet at her through a window."

"And what did you do after that?" I asked, when he had paused for a long time with his chin on his breast.

"Well," said he, "I did a lot of thinking them days, and I says to myself: 'This thing is wrong, and I will go out and stop it — I will go out and stop it.'"

As he uttered these words, I looked at him

curiously — his absurd flat fur hat with the moth-eaten ears, the old bulging overcoat, the round spectacles, the scarred, insignificant face — he seemed somehow transformed, a person elevated above himself, the tool of some vast incalculable force.

I shall never forget the phrase he used to describe his own feelings when he had reached this astonishing decision to go out and stop the wrongs of the world. He said he "began to feel all clean inside."

"I see it didn't matter what become o' me, and I began to feel all clean inside."

It seemed, he explained, as though something big and strong had got hold of him, and he began to be happy.

"Since then," he said in a low voice, "I've been happier than I ever was before in all my life. I ain't got any family, nor any home — rightly speakin' — nor any money, but, comrade, you see here in front of you, a happy man."

When he had finished his story we sat quiet for some time.

"Well," said he, finally, "I must be goin'. The committee will wonder what's become o' me."

I followed him out to the road. There I put my hand on his shoulder, and said:

"Bill Hahn, you are a better man than I am."

He smiled, a beautiful smile, and we walked off together down the road.

I wish I had gone on with him at that time into the city, but somehow I could not do it. I stopped near the top of the hill where one can see in the distance that smoky huddle of buildings which is known as Kilburn, and though he urged me, I turned aside and sat down in the edge of a meadow. There were many things I wanted to think about, to get clear in my mind.

As I sat looking out toward that great city, I saw three men walking in the white road. As I watched them, I could see them coming quickly, eagerly. Presently they threw up their hands and evidently began to shout, though I could not hear what they said. At that moment I saw my friend Bill Hahn running in the road, his coat skirts flapping heavily about his legs. When they met they almost fell into one another's arms.

I suppose it was so that the early Christians, those who hid in the Roman catacombs, were wont to greet one another.

So I sat thinking.

"A man," I said to myself, "who can regard himself as a function, not an end of creation, has arrived."

After a time I got up and walked down the hill — some strange force carrying me onward — and came thus to the city of Kilburn.

I AM CAUGHT UP INTO LIFE

CHAPTER X

I AM CAUGHT UP INTO LIFE

I CAN scarcely convey in written words the whirling emotions I felt when I entered the city of Kilburn. Every sight, every sound, recalled vividly and painfully the unhappy years I had once spent in another and greater city. Every mingled odour of the streets — and there is nothing that will so surely re-create (for me) the inner emotion of a time or place as a remembered odour — brought back to me the incidents of that immemorial existence.

For a time, I confess it frankly here, I

felt afraid.   More than once I stopped short
in the street where I was walking, and considered turning about and making again for
the open country.   Some there may be who
will feel that I am exaggerating my sensations
and impressions, but they do not know of my
memories of a former life, nor of how, many
years ago, I left the city quite defeated,
glad indeed that I was escaping, and thinking
(as I have related elsewhere) that I should
never again set foot upon a paved street.
These things went deep with me. Only
the other day, when a friend asked me how
old I was, I responded instantly — our un-
premeditated words are usually truest — with
the date of my arrival at this farm.

"Then you are only ten years old!" he exclaimed with a laugh, thinking I was joking.

"Well," I said, "I am counting only the
years worth living."

No; I existed, but I never really lived
until I was reborn, that wonderful summer,
here among these hills.

I said I felt afraid in the streets of Kilburn, but it was no physical fear. Who
could be safer in a city than the man who
has not a penny in his pockets? It was

rather a strange, deep, spiritual shrinking. There seemed something so irresistible about this life of the city, so utterly overpowering. I had a sense of being smaller than I had previously felt myself, that in some way my personality, all that was strong or interesting or original about me, was being smudged over, rubbed out. In the country I had in some measure come to command life, but here, it seemed to me, life was commanding me and crushing me down. It is a difficult thing to describe: I never felt just that way before.

I stopped at last on the main street of Kilburn in the very heart of the town. I stopped because it seemed necessary to me, like a man in a flood, to touch bottom, to get hold upon something immovable and stable. It was just at that hour of evening when the stores and shops are pouring forth their rivulets of humanity to join the vast flood of the streets. I stepped quickly aside into a niche near the corner of an immense building of brick and steel and glass, and there I stood with my back to the wall, and I watched the restless, whirling, torrential tide of the streets. I felt again, as I had not felt it before in years, the mysterious urge of the city — the sense of unending, overpowering movement.

There was another strange, indeed uncanny, sensation that began to creep over me as I stood there. Though hundreds upon hundreds of men and women were passing me every minute, not one of them seemed to see me. Most of them did not even look in my direction, and those who did turn their eyes toward me seemed to glance through me to the building behind. I wonder if this is at all a common experience, or whether I was unduly sensitive that day, unduly wrought up? I began to feel like one clad in garments of invisibility. I could see, but was not seen. I could feel, but was not felt. In the country there are few who would not stop to speak to me, or at least appraise me with their eyes; but here I was a wraith, a ghost — not a palpable human being at all. For a moment I felt unutterably lonely.

It is this way with me. When I have reached the very depths of any serious situation or tragic emotion, something within me seems at last to stop — how shall I describe it? — and I rebound suddenly and see the world, as it were, double — see that my condition instead of being serious or tragic is in reality amusing — and I usually came out of it with an utterly absurd or whimsical idea. It was so upon this occasion. I think it was the image of my robust self as a wraith that did it.

"After all," I said aloud taking a firm hold on the good hard flesh of one of my legs, "this is positively David Grayson."

I looked out again into that tide of faces — interesting, tired, passive, smiling, sad, but above all, preoccupied faces.

"No one," I thought, "seems to know that David Grayson has come to town."

I had the sudden, almost irresistible notion of climbing up a step near me, holding up one hand, and crying out:

"Here I am, my friends. I am David Grayson. I am real and solid and opaque; I have plenty of red blood running in my veins. I assure you that I am a person well worth knowing."

I should really have enjoyed some such outlandish enterprise, and I am not at all sure yet that it would not have brought

me adventures and made me friends worth
while. We fail far more often by under-daring
than by over-daring.

But this imaginary object had the result,
at least, of giving me a new grip on things.
I began to look out upon the amazing spectacle before me in a different mood. It was
exactly like some enormous anthill into which
an idle traveller had thrust his cane. Everywhere the ants were running out of their
tunnels and burrows, many carrying burdens
and giving one strangely the impression
that while they were intensely alive and
active, not more than half of them had any
clear idea of where they were going. And
serious, deadly serious, in their haste! I felt
a strong inclination to stop a few of them
and say:

"Friends, cheer up. It isn't half as bad
as you think it is. Cheer up!"

After a time the severity of the human
flood began to abate, and here and there
at the bottom of that gulch of a street,
which had begun to fill with soft, bluish-
gray shadows, the evening lights appeared.
The air had grown cooler; in the distance
around a corner I heard a street organ break

suddenly and joyously into the lively strains of "The Wearin' o' the Green."

I stepped out into the street with quite a new feeling of adventure. And as if to testify that I was now a visible person a sharp-eyed newsboy discovered me — the first human being in Kilburn who had actually seen me — and came up with a paper in his hand.

"*Herald*, boss?"

I was interested in the shrewd, world-wise, humorous look in the urchin's eyes.

"No," I began, with the full intent of bantering him into some sort of acquaintance; but he evidently measured my purchasing capacity quite accurately, for he turned like a flash to another customer.

"*Herald*, boss?"

"You'll have to step lively, David Grayson," I said to myself, "if you get aboard in this city."

A slouchy negro with a cigarette in his fingers glanced at me in passing and then, hesitating, turned quickly toward me.

"Got a match, boss?"

I gave him a match.

"Thank you, boss," and he passed on down the street.

"I seem to be 'boss' around here," I said.

This contact, slight as it was, gave me a feeling of warmth, removed a little the sensation of aloofness I had felt, and I strolled slowly down the street, looking in at the gay windows, now ablaze with lights, and watching the really wonderful procession of vehicles of all shapes and sizes that rattled by on the pavement. Even at that hour of the day I think there were more of them in one minute than I see in a whole month at my farm.

It's a great thing to wear shabby clothes and an old hat. Some of the best things I have ever known, like these experiences of the streets, have resulted from coming up to life from underneath; of being taken for less than I am rather than for more than I am.

I did not always believe in this doctrine. For many years — the years before I was rightly born into this alluring world — I tried quite the opposite course. I was constantly attempting to come down to life from above. Instead of being content to carry through life a sufficiently wonderful being named David Grayson I tried desperately to set up and support a sort of dummy creature which, so clad, so housed, so fed, should appear to be what I thought David Grayson ought to appear in the eyes of the world. Oh, I spent quite a lifetime trying to satisfy other people!

Once I remember staying at home, in bed, reading "Huckleberry Finn," while I sent my trousers out to be mended.

Well, that dummy Grayson perished in a cornfield. His empty coat served well for a scarecrow. A wisp of straw stuck out through a hole in his finest hat.

And I — the man within — I escaped, and have been out freely upon the great adventure of life.

If a shabby coat (and I speak here also symbolically, not forgetful of spiritual significances) lets you into the adventurous world of those who are poor it does not on the other hand rob you of any true friendship among those who are rich or mighty. I say true friendship, for unless a man who is rich and mighty is able to see through my shabby coat (as I see through his fine one), I shall gain nothing by knowing him.

I've permitted myself all this digression — left myself walking alone there in the streets of Kilburn while I philosophized upon the ways and means of life — not without design, for I could have had no such experiences as I did have in Kilburn if I had worn a better coat or carried upon me the evidences of security in life.

I think I have already remarked upon the extraordinary enlivement of wits which comes to the man who has been without a meal or so and does not know when or where he is again to break his fast. Try it, friend, and see! It was already getting along in the evening, and I knew or supposed I knew no one in Kilburn save only Bill Hahn, Socialist, who was little better off than I was.

In this emergency my mind began to work swiftly. A score of fascinating plans for getting my supper and a bed to sleep in flashed through my mind.

"Why," said I, "when I come to think of it, I'm comparatively rich. I'll warrant there are plenty of places in Kilburn, and good ones, too, where I could barter a chapter of Montaigne and a little good conversation for a first-rate supper, and I've no doubt that I could whistle up a bed almost anywhere!"

I thought of a little motto I often repeat to myself:

To know life, begin anywhere!

There were several people on the streets of Kilburn that night who don't know yet how very near they were to being boarded by a somewhat shabby looking farmer who would have offered them, let us say, a notable musical production called "Old Dan Tucker," exquisitely performed on a tin whistle, in exchange for a good honest supper.

There was one man in particular — a fine, pompous citizen who came down the street swinging his cane and looking as though the universe was a sort of Christmas turkey, lying all brown and sizzling before him ready to be carved — a fine pompous citizen who never realized how nearly Fate with a battered volume of Montaigne in one hand and a tin whistle in the other — came to pouncing upon him that evening! And I am firmly convinced that if I had attacked him with the Great Particular Word he would have carved me off a juicy slice of the white breast meat.

"I'm getting hungry," I said; "I must find Bill Hahn!"

I had turned down a side street, and seeing there in front of a building a number of lounging men with two or three cabs or carriages standing nearby in the street I walked up to them. It was a livery barn.

Now I like all sorts of out-of-door people: I seem to be related to them through horses and cattle and cold winds and sunshine. I like them and understand them, and they seem to like me and understand me. So I walked up to the group of jolly drivers and stablemen intending to ask my directions. The talking died out and they all turned to look at me. I suppose I was not altogether a familiar type there in the city streets. My bag, especially, seemed to set me apart as a curious person.

"Friends," I said, "I am a farmer —— "

They all broke out laughing; they seemed to know it already! I was just a little taken aback, but I laughed, too, knowing that there was a way of getting at them if only I could find it.

"It may surprise you," I said, "but this

is the first time in some dozen years that I've been in a big city like this."

"You nadn't 'ave told us, partner!" said one of them, evidently the wit of the group, in a rich Irish brogue.

"Well," I responded, laughing with the rest of them, "you've been living right here all the time, and don't realize how amusing and curious the city looks to me. Why, I feel as though I had been away sleeping for twenty years, like Rip Van Winkle. When I left the city there was scarcely an automobile to be seen anywhere — and now look at them snorting through the streets. I counted twenty-two passing that corner up there in five minutes by the clock."

This was a fortunate remark, for I found instantly that the invasion of the automobile was a matter of tremendous import to such Knights of Bucephalus as these.

At first the wit interrupted me with amusing remarks, as wits will, but I soon had him as quiet as the others. For I have found the things that chiefly interest people are the things they already know about — provided you show them that these common things are still mysterious, still miraculous, as indeed they are.

After a time some one pushed me a stable stool and I sat down among them, and we had quite a conversation, which finally developed into an amusing comparison (I wish I had room to repeat it here) between the city and the country. I told them something about my farm, how much I enjoyed it, and what a wonderful free life one had in the country. In this I was really taking an unfair advantage of them, for I was trading on the fact that every man, down deep in his heart, has more or less of an instinct to get back to the soil — at least all outdoor men have. And when I described the simplest things about my barn, and the cattle and pigs, and the bees — and the good things we have to eat — I had every one of them leaning forward and hanging on my words.

Harriet sometimes laughs at me for the way I celebrate farm life. She says all my apples are the size of Hubbard squashes, my eggs all double-yolked, and my cornfields tropical jungles. Practical Harriet! My apples may not *all* be the size of Hubbard squashes, but they are good, sizable apples, and as

for flavour — all the spices of Arcady —— !
And I believe, I *know*, from my own experience that these fields and hills are capable
of healing men's souls. And when I see people wandering around a lonesome city like
Kilburn, with never a soft bit of soil to
put their heels into, nor a green thing to cultivate, nor any corn or apples or honey to
harvest, I feel — well, that they are wasting
their time.

(It's a fact, Harriet!)

Indeed, I had the most curious experience with my friend the wit — his name
I soon learned was Healy — a jolly, round,
red-nosed, outdoor chap with fists that looked
like small-sized hams, and a rich, warm
Irish voice. At first he was inclined to use
me as the ready butt of his lively mind,
but presently he became so much interested
in what I was saying that he sat squarely
in front of me with both his jolly eyes and
his smiling mouth wide open.

"If ever you pass my way," I said to
him, "just drop in and I'll give you a dinner of baked beans" — and I smacked —"and
home made bread" — and I smacked again

— "and pumpkin pie" — and I smacked a third time — "that will make your mouth water."

All this smacking and the description of baked beans and pumpkin pie had an odd counter effect upon *me;* for I suddenly recalled my own tragic state.   So I jumped up quickly and asked directions for getting down to the mill neighbourhood, where I hoped to find Bill Hahn.   My friend Healy instantly volunteered the information.

"And now," I said, "I want to ask a small favour of you.   I'm looking for a friend, and I'd like to leave my bag here for the night."

"Sure, sure," said the Irishman heartily. "Put it there in the office — on top o' the desk.   It'll be all right."

So I put it in the office and was about to say good-bye, when my friend said to me:

"Come in, partner, and have a drink before you go" — and he pointed to a nearby saloon.

"Thank you," I answered heartily, for I knew it was as fine a bit of hospitality as he could offer me, "thank you, but I must find my friend before it gets too late."

"Aw, come on now," he cried, taking

my arm. "Sure you'll be better off for a bit o' warmth inside."

I had hard work to get away from them, and I am as sure as can be that they would have found supper and a bed for me if they had known I needed either.

"Come agin," Healy shouted after me, "we're glad to see a farmer any toime."

My way led me quickly out of the well-groomed and glittering main streets of the town. I passed first through several blocks of quiet residences, and then came to a street near the river which was garishly lighted, and crowded with small, poor shops and stores, with a saloon on nearly every corner. I passed a huge, dark, silent box of a mill, and I saw what I never saw before in a city, armed men guarding the streets.

Although it was growing late — it was after nine o'clock — crowds of people were still parading the streets, and there was something intangibly restless, something tense, in the very atmosphere of the neighbourhood. It was very plain that I had reached the strike district. I was about to make some further inquiries for the headquarters of the mill men or for Bill Hahn personally, when I saw, not far ahead of me, a black crowd of people reaching out into the street. Drawing nearer I saw that an open space or block between two rows of houses was literally black with human beings, and in the centre on a raised platform, under a gasolene flare, I beheld my friend of the road, Bill Hahn. The overcoat and the hat with the furry ears had disappeared, and the little man stood there, bareheaded, before that great audience.

My experience in the world is limited, but I have never heard anything like that speech for sheer power. It was as unruly and powerful and resistless as life itself. It was not like any other speech I ever heard, for it was no mere giving out by the orator of ideas and thoughts and feelings of his own. It seemed rather — how shall I describe it? — as though the speaker was looking into the very hearts of that vast gathering of poor men and poor women and merely telling them what they themselves felt, but could not tell. And I shall never forget the breathless hush of the people or the quality of their responses to the orator's words. It was as though they said, "Yes, yes" — with a feeling of vast relief — "Yes, yes — at last our own

hopes and fears and desires are being uttered—
yes, yes."

As for the orator himself, he held up one
maimed hand and leaned over the edge of
the platform, and his undistinguished face
glowed with the white light of a great passion
within. The man had utterly forgotten himself.

I confess, among those eager working
people, clad in their poor garments, I confess I was profoundly moved. Faith is not
so bounteous a commodity in this world
that we can afford to treat even its unfamiliar
manifestations with contempt. And when
a movement is hot with life, when it stirs
common men to their depths, look out! look
out!

Up to that time I had never known much
of the practical workings of Socialism; and
the main contention of its philosophy has
never accorded wholly with my experience
in life.

But the Socialism of to-day is no mere
intellectual abstraction — as it was, perhaps,
in the days of Brook Farm. It is a mode of
action. Men whose view of life is perfectly
balanced rarely soil themselves with the

dust of battle. The heat necessary to produce social conflict (and social progress —
who knows?) is generated by a supreme faith
that certain principles are universal in their
application when in reality they are only local
or temporary.

Thus while one may not accept the philosophy of Socialism as a final explanation of
human life, he may yet look upon Socialism in action as a powerful method of stimu-
lating human progress. The world has been
lagging behind in its sense of brotherhood,
and we now have the Socialists knit together
in a fighting friendship as fierce and narrow
in its motives as Calvinism, pricking us to
reform, asking the cogent question:

"Are we not all brothers?"

Oh, we are going a long way with these
Socialists, we are going to discover a new
world of social relationships — and then, and
then, like a mighty wave, will flow in upon us
a renewed and more wonderful sense of the
worth of the individual human soul. A new
individualism, bringing with it, perhaps, some
faint realization of our dreams of a race of
Supermen, lies just beyond! Its prophets,
girded with rude garments and feeding upon

the wild honey of poverty, are already crying in the wilderness.

I think I could have remained there at the Socialist meeting all night long: there was something about it that brought a hard, dry twist to my throat. But after a time my friend Bill Hahn, evidently quite worn out, yielded his place to another and far less clairvoyant speaker, and the crowd, among whom I now discovered quite a number of policemen, began to thin out.

I made my way forward and saw Bill Hahn and several other men just leaving the platform. I stepped up to him, but it was not until I called him by name (I knew how absent minded he was!) that he recognized me.

"Well, well," he said; "you came after all!"

He seized me by both arms and introduced me to several of his companions as "Brother Grayson." They all shook hands with me warmly.

Although he was perspiring, Bill put on his overcoat and the old fur hat with the ears, and as he now took my arm I could feel one of his bulging pockets beating against my leg. I had not the slightest idea where they were going, but Bill held me by the arm and presently we came, a block or so distant, to a dark, narrow stairway leading up from the street. I recall the stumbling sound of steps on the wooden boards, a laugh or two, the high voice of a woman asserting and denying. Feeling our way along the wall, we came to the top and went into a long, low, rather dimly lighted room set about with tables and chairs — a sort of restaurant. A number of men and a few women had already gathered there. Among them my eyes instantly singled out a huge, rough-looking man who stood at the centre of an animated group. He had thick, shaggy hair, and one side of his face over the cheekbone was of a dull blue-black and raked and scarred, where it had been burned in a powder blast. He had been a miner. His gray eyes, which had a surprisingly youthful and even humorous expression, looked out from under coarse, thick, gray brows. A very remarkable face and figure he presented. I soon learned that he was R —— D ——, the leader of whom I had often heard, and heard no good thing. He was quite a different type from Bill Hahn:

" A huge, rough-looking man . . . stood at the centre of an animated group "

he was the man of authority, the organizer, the diplomat — as Bill was the prophet, preaching a holy war.

How wonderful human nature is! Only a short time before I had been thrilled by the intensity of the passion of the throng, but here the mood suddenly changed to one of friendly gayety. Fully a third of those present were women, some of them plainly from the mills and some of them curiously different — women from other walks in life who had thrown themselves heart and soul into the strike. Without ceremony but with much laughing and joking, they found their places around the tables. A cook who appeared in a dim doorway was greeted with a shout, to which he responded with a wide smile, waving the long spoon which he held in his hand.

I shall not attempt to give any complete description of the gathering or of what they said or did. I think I could devote a dozen pages to the single man who was placed next to me. I was interested in him from the outset. The first thing that struck me about him was an air of neatness, even fastidiousness, about his person — though he wore no stiff collar, only a soft woollen shirt without a necktie. He had the long, sensitive, beautiful hands of an artist, but his face was thin and marked with the pallor peculiar to the indoor worker. I soon learned that he was a weaver in the mills, an Englishman by birth, and we had not talked two minutes before I found that, while he had never had any education in the schools, he had been a gluttonous reader of books — all kinds of books — and, what is more, had thought about them and was ready with vigorous (and narrow) opinions about this author or that. And he knew more about economics and sociology, I firmly believe, than half the college professors. A truly remarkable man.

It was an Italian restaurant, and I remember how, in my hunger, I assailed the generous dishes of boiled meat and spaghetti. A red wine was served in large bottles which circulated rapidly around the table, and almost immediately the room began to fill with tobacco smoke. Every one seemed to be talking and laughing at once, in the liveliest spirit of good fellowship. They joked from table to table, and sometimes the whole room would quiet down while

some one told a joke, which invariably wound
up with a roar of laughter.

"Why," I said, "these people have a
whole life, a whole society, of their own!"

In the midst of this jollity the clear voice
of a girl rang out with the first lines of a
song. Instantly the room was hushed:

> Arise, ye prisoners of starvation,
>   Arise, ye wretched of the earth,
> For justice thunders condemnation
>   A better world's in birth.

These were the words she sang, and when
the clear, sweet voice died down the whole
company, as though by a common impulse,
arose from their chairs, and joined in a great
swelling chorus:

> It is the final conflict,
>   Let each stand in his place,
> The Brotherhood of Man
>   Shall be the human race.

It was beyond belief, to me, the spirit
with which these words were sung. In no
sense with jollity — all that seemed to have
been dropped when they came to their feet —
but with an unmistakable fervour of faith.
Some of the things I had thought and dreamed
about secretly among the hills of my farm

all these years, dreamed about as being something far off and as unrealizable as the millennium, were here being sung abroad with jaunty faith by these weavers of Kilburn, these weavers and workers whom I had schooled myself to regard with a sort of distant pity.

Hardly had the company sat down again, with a renewal of the flow of jolly conversation when I heard a rapping on one of the tables. I saw the great form of R —— D —— slowly rising.

"Brothers and sisters," he said, "a word of caution. The authorities will lose no chance of putting us in the wrong. Above all we must comport ourselves here and in the strike with great care. We are fighting a great battle, bigger than we are —— "

At this instant the door from the dark hallway suddenly opened and a man in a policeman's uniform stepped in. There fell an instant's dead silence — an explosive silence. Every person there seemed to be petrified in the position in which his attention was attracted. Every eye was fixed on the figure at the door. For an instant no one said a word; then I heard a woman's shrill voice, like a rifle-shot:

"Assassin!"

I cannot imagine what might have happened next, for the feeling in the room, as in the city itself, was at the tensest, had not the leader suddenly brought the goblet which he held in his hand down with a bang upon the table.

"As I was saying," he continued in a steady, clear voice, "we are fighting today the greatest of battles, and we cannot permit trivial incidents, or personal bitterness, or small persecutions, to turn us from the great work we have in hand. However our opponents may comport themselves, we must be calm, steady, sure, patient, for we know that our cause is just and will prevail."

"You're right," shouted a voice back in the room.

Instantly the tension relaxed, conversation started again and every one turned away from the policeman at the door. In a few minutes, he disappeared without having said a word.

There was no regular speaking, and about midnight the party began to break up. I leaned over and said to my friend Bill Hahn:

"Can you find me a place to sleep to-night?"

"Certainly I can," he said heartily.

There was to be a brief conference of the leaders after the supper, and most of those present soon departed. I went down the long, dark stairway and out into the almost deserted street. Looking up between the buildings I could see the clear blue sky and the stars. And I walked slowly up and down awaiting my friend and trying, vainly, to calm my whirling emotions.

He came at last and I went with him. That night I slept scarcely at all, but lay looking up into the darkness. And it seemed as though, as I lay there, listening, that I could hear the city moving in its restless sleep, and sighing as with heavy pain. All night long I lay there thinking.

I GRAPPLE WITH THE CITY

CHAPTER XI

I GRAPPLE WITH THE CITY

I HAVE laughed heartily many times since
I came home to think of the Figure of
Tragedy I felt myself that morning in the
city of Kilburn. I had not slept well, had
not slept at all, I think, and the experiences
and emotions of the previous night still
lay heavy upon me. Not before in many
years had I felt such a depression of the
spirits.

It was all so different from the things I
love! Not so much as a spear of grass or a
leafy tree to comfort the eye, or a bird to

sing; no quiet hills, no sight of the sun coming up in the morning over dewy fields, no sound of cattle in the lane, no cheerful cackling of fowls, nor buzzing of bees! That morning, I remember, when I first went out into those squalid streets and saw everywhere the evidences of poverty, dirt, and ignorance — and the sweet, clean country not two miles away — the thought of my own home among the hills (with Harriet there in the doorway) came upon me with incredible longing.

"I must go home; I must go home!" I caught myself saying aloud.

I remember how glad I was when I found that my friend Bill Hahn and other leaders of the strike were to be engaged in conferences during the forenoon, for I wanted to be alone, to try to get a few things straightened out in my mind.

But I soon found that a city is a poor place for reflection or contemplation. It bombards one with an infinite variety of new impressions and new adventures; and I could not escape the impression made by crowded houses, and ill-smelling streets, and dirty sidewalks, and swarming human beings. For a time the burden of these things rested upon my breast like a leaden weight; they all seemed so utterly wrong to me, so unnecessary, so unjust! I sometimes think of religion as only a high sense of good order; and it seemed to me that morning as though the very existence of this disorderly mill district was a challenge to religion, and an offence to the Orderer of an Orderly Universe. I don't know how such conditions may affect other people, but for a time I felt a sharp sense of impatience — yes, anger — with it all. I had an impulse to take off my coat then and there and go at the job of setting things to rights. Oh, I never was more serious in my life: I was quite prepared to change the entire scheme of things to my way of thinking whether the people who lived there liked it or not. It seemed to me for a few glorious moments that I had only to tell them of the wonders in our country, the pleasant, quiet roads, the comfortable farmhouses, the fertile fields, and the wooded hills — and, poof! all this crowded poverty would dissolve and disappear, and they would all come to the country and be as happy as I was.

I remember how, once in my life, I wasted untold energy trying to make over my dearest friends. There was Harriet, for example, dear, serious, practical Harriet. I used to be fretted by the way she was forever trying to clip my wing feathers — I suppose to keep me close to the quiet and friendly and unadventurous roost! We come by such a long, long road, sometimes, to the acceptance of our nearest friends for exactly what they are. Because we are so fond of them we try to make them over to suit some curious ideal of perfection of our own — until one day we suddenly laugh aloud at our own absurdity (knowing that they are probably trying as hard to reconstruct us as we are to reconstruct them!) and thereafter we try no more to change them, we just love 'em and enjoy 'em!

Some such psychological process went on in my consciousness that morning. As I walked briskly through the streets I began to look out more broadly around me. It was really a perfect spring morning, the air crisp, fresh, and sunny, and the streets full of life and activity. I looked into the faces of the people I met, and it began to strike me that most of them seemed oblivious of the fact that they should, by good rights, be looking downcast and dispirited. They had cheered their approval the night before when the speakers had told them how miserable they were (even acknowledging that they were slaves), and yet here they were this morning looking positively good-humoured, cheerful, some of them even gay. I warrant if I had stepped up to one of them that morning and intimated that he was a slave he would have — well, I should have had serious trouble with him! There was a degree of sociability in those back streets, a visiting from window to window, gossipy gatherings in front areaways, a sort of pavement domesticity, that I had never seen before. Being a lover myself of such friendly intercourse I could actually feel the human warmth of that neighbourhood.

A group of brightly clad girl strikers gathered on a corner were chatting and laughing, and children in plenty ran and shouted at their play in the street. I saw a group of them dancing merrily around an Italian hand-organ man who was filling the air with jolly music. I recall what a sinking sensation I had at

the pit of my reformer's stomach when it suddenly occurred to me that these people,
some of them, anyway, might actually *like*
this crowded, sociable neighbourhood! "They
might even *hate* the country," I exclaimed.

It is surely one of the fundamental humours of life to see absurdly serious little
human beings (like D. G. for example) trying to stand in the place of the Almighty.
We are so confoundedly infallible in our judg-
ments, so sure of what is good for our neighbour, so eager to force upon him our particular doctors or our particular remedies;
we are so willing to put our childish fingers
into the machinery of creation — and we howl
so lustily when we get them pinched!

"Why!" I exclaimed, for it came to me
like a new discovery, "it's exactly the same
here as it is in the country! I haven't got
to make over the universe: I've only got to
do my own small job, and to look up often
at the trees and the hills and the sky and
be friendly with all men."

I cannot express the sense of comfort,
and of trust, which this reflection brought
me. I recall stopping just then at the corner
of a small green city square, for I had now

reached the better part of the city, and of seeing with keen pleasure the green of the grass and the bright colour of a bed of flowers, and two or three clean nursemaids with clean baby cabs, and a flock of pigeons pluming themselves near a stone fountain, and an old tired horse sleeping in the sun with his nose buried in a feed bag.

"Why," I said, "all this, too, is beautiful!"

So I continued my walk with quite a new feeling in my heart, prepared again for any adventure life might have to offer me.

I supposed I knew no living soul in Kilburn but Bill the Socialist. What was my astonishment and pleasure, then, in one of the business streets to discover a familiar face and figure. A man was just stepping from an automobile to the sidewalk. For an instant, in that unusual environment, I could not place him, then I stepped up quickly and said:

"Well, well, Friend Vedder."

He looked around with astonishment at the man in the shabby clothes — but it was only for an instant.

"David Grayson!" he exclaimed, "and how did *you* get into the city?"

"Walked," I said.

"But I thought you were an incurable and irreproachable countryman! Why are you here?"

"Love o' life," I said; "love o' life."

"Where are you stopping?"

I waved my hand.

"Where the road leaves me," I said. "Last night I left my bag with some good friends I made in front of a livery stable and I spent the night in the mill district with a Socialist named Bill Hahn."

"Bill Hahn!" The effect upon Mr. Vedder was magical.

"Why, yes," I said, "and a remarkable man he is, too."

I discovered immediately that my friend was quite as much interested in the strike as Bill Hahn, but on the other side. He was, indeed, one of the directors of the greatest mill in Kilburn — the very one which I had seen the night before surrounded by armed sentinels. It was thrilling to me, this knowledge, for it seemed to plump me down at once in the middle of things — and soon, indeed, brought me nearer to the brink of great events than ever I was before in all my days.

I could see that Mr. Vedder considered Bill Hahn as a sort of devouring monster, a wholly incendiary and dangerous person. So terrible, indeed, was the warning he gave me (considering me, I suppose an unsophisticated person) that I couldn't help laughing outright.

"I assure you —— " he began, apparently much offended.

But I interrupted him.

"I'm sorry I laughed," I said, "but as you were talking about Bill Hahn, I couldn't help thinking of him as I first saw him." And I gave Mr. Vedder as lively a description as I could of the little man with his bulging coat tails, his furry ears, his odd round spectacles. He was greatly interested in what I said and began to ask many questions. I told him with all the earnestness I could command of Bill's history and of his conversion to his present beliefs. I found that Mr. Vedder had known Robert Winter very well indeed, and was amazed at the incident which I narrated of Bill Hahn's attempt upon his life.

I have always believed that if men could be made to understand one another they would necessarily be friendly, so I did my best to explain Bill Hahn to Mr. Vedder.

"I'm tremendously interested in what you say," he said, "and we must have more talk about it."

He told me that he had now to put in an appearance at his office, and wanted me to go with him; but upon my objection he pressed me to take luncheon with him a little later, an invitation which I accepted with real pleasure.

"We haven't had a word about gardens," he said, "and there are no end of things that Mrs. Vedder and I found that we wanted to talk with you about after you had left us."

"Well," I said, much delighted, "let's have a regular old-fashioned country talk."

So we parted for the time being, and I set off in the highest spirits to see something more of Kilburn.

A city, after all, is a very wonderful place. One thing, I recall, impressed me powerfully that morning — the way in which every one was working, apparently without any common agreement or any common purpose, and yet with a high sort of understanding. The first hearing of a difficult piece of music (to an uncultivated ear like mine) often yields nothing but a confused sense of unrelated motives, but later and deeper hearings reveal the harmony which ran so clear in the master's soul.

Something of this sort happened to me in looking out upon the life of that great city of Kilburn. All about on the streets, in the buildings, under ground and above ground, men were walking, running, creeping, crawling, climbing, lifting, digging, driving, buying, selling, sweating, swearing, praying, loving, hating, struggling, failing, sinning, repenting — all working and living according to a vast harmony, which sometimes we can catch clearly and sometimes miss entirely. I think, that morning, for a time, I heard the true music of the spheres, the stars singing together.

Mr. Vedder took me to a quiet restaurant where we had a snug alcove all to ourselves. I shall remember it always as one of the truly pleasant experiences of my pilgrimage.

I could see that my friend was sorely troubled, that the strike rested heavy upon him, and so I led the conversation to the hills and the roads and the fields we both love so much. I plied him with a thousand questions about his garden. I told him in the liveliest way of my adventures after leaving his home, how I had telephoned him from the hills, how I had taken a swim in the mill-pond, and especially how I had lost myself in the old cowpasture, with an account of all my absurd and laughable adventures and emotions.

Well, before we had finished our luncheon I had every line ironed from the brow of that poor plagued rich man, I had brought jolly crinkles to the corners of his eyes, and once or twice I had him chuckling down deep inside (where chuckles are truly effective). Talk about cheering up the poor: I think the rich are usually far more in need of it!

But I couldn't keep the conversation in these delightful channels. Evidently the strike and all that it meant lay heavy upon Mr. Vedder's consciousness, for he pushed back his coffee and began talking about it, almost in a tone of apology. He told me how kind he had tried to make the mill management in its dealings with its men.

"I would not speak of it save in explanation of our true attitude of helpfulness; but we have really given our men many advantages"— and he told me of the reading-room the company had established, of the visiting nurse they had employed, and of several other excellent enterprises, which gave only another proof of what I knew already of Mr. Vedder's sincere kindness of heart.

"But," he said, "we find they don't appreciate what we try to do for them."

I laughed outright.

"Why," I exclaimed, "you are having the same trouble I have had!"

"How's that?" he inquired, I thought a little sharply. Men don't like to have their seriousness trifled with.

"No longer ago than this morning," I said, "I had exactly that idea of giving them advantages; but I found that the difficulty lies not with the ability to give, but with the inability or unwillingness to take. You see I have a great deal of surplus wealth my- self ——"

Mr. Vedder's eyes flickered up at me.

"Yes," I said. "I've got immense accumulations of the wealth of the ages — ingots of Emerson and Whitman, for example, gems of Voltaire, and I can't tell what other superfluous coinage!" (And I waved my hand in the most grandiloquent manner.) "I've also quite a store of knowledge of corn and calves and cucumbers, and I've a boundless domain of exceedingly valuable landscapes. I am prepared to give bountifully of all these varied riches (for I shall still have plenty remaining), but the fact is that this generation of vipers doesn't appreciate what I am trying to do for them. I'm really getting frightened, lest they permit me to perish from undistributed riches!"

Mr. Vedder was still smiling.

"Oh," I said, warming up to my idea, "I'm a regular multimillionaire. I've got so much wealth that I'm afraid I shall not be as fortunate as jolly Andy Carnegie, for I don't see how I can possibly die poor!"

"Why not found a university or so?" asked Mr. Vedder.

"Well, I had thought of that. It's a good idea. Let's join our forces and establish a university where truly serious people can take courses in laughter."

"Fine idea!" exclaimed Mr. Vedder; "but wouldn't it require an enormous endowment to accommodate all the applicants? You must remember that this is a very benighted and illiterate world, laughingly speaking."

"It is, indeed," I said, "but you must remember that many people, for a long time, will be too serious to apply. I wonder sometimes if any one ever learns to laugh— *really* laugh — much before he is forty."

"But," said Mr. Vedder anxiously, "do you think such an institution would be accepted by the proletariat of the serious-minded?"

"Ah, that's the trouble," said I, "that's the trouble. The proletariat doesn't appreciate what we are trying to do for them! They don't want your reading-rooms nor my Emerson and cucumbers. The seat of the difficulty seems to be that what seems wealth to us isn't necessarily wealth for the other fellow."

I cannot tell with what delight we fenced our way through this foolery (which was not all foolery, either). I never met a man more quickly responsive than Mr. Vedder. But he now paused for some moments, evidently ruminating.

"Well, David," he said seriously, "what

are we going to do about this obstreperous other fellow?"

"Why not try the experiment," I suggested, "of giving him what he considers wealth, instead of what you consider wealth?"

"But what does he consider wealth?"

"Equality," said I.

Mr. Vedder threw up his hands.

"So you're a Socialist, too!"

"That," I said, "is another story."

"Well, supposing we did or could give him this equality you speak of — what would become of us? What would we get out of it?"

"Why, equality, too!" I said.

Mr. Vedder threw up his hands with a gesture of mock resignation.

"Come," said he, "let's get down out of Utopia!"

We had some further good-humoured fencing and then returned to the inevitable problem of the strike. While we were discussing the meeting of the night before which, I learned, had been luridly reported in the morning papers, Mr. Vedder suddenly turned to me and asked earnestly:

"Are you really a Socialist?"

"Well," said I, "I'm sure of one thing. I'm not *all* Socialist. Bill Hahn believes with his whole soul (and his faith has made him a remarkable man) that if only another class of people — his class — could come into the control of material property, that all the ills that man is heir to would be speedily cured. But I wonder if when men own property collectively — as they are going to one of these days — they will quarrel and hate one another any less than they do now. It is not the ownership of material property that interests me so much as the independence of it. When I started out from my farm on this pilgrimage it seemed to me the most blessed thing in the world to get away from property and possession."

"What are you then, anyway?" asked Mr. Vedder, smiling.

"Well, I've thought of a name I would like to have applied to me sometimes," I said. "You see I'm tremendously fond of this world exactly as it is now. Mr. Vedder, it's a wonderful and beautiful place! I've never seen a better one. I confess I could not possibly live in the rarefied atmosphere of a final solution. I want to live right here and now for all I'm worth. The other day a man asked me what I thought was the best time of life. 'Why,' I answered without a thought, 'Now.' It has always seemed to me that if a man can't make a go of it, yes, and be happy at this moment, he can't be at the next moment. But most of all, it seems to me, I want to get close to people, to look into their hearts, and be friendly with them. Mr. Vedder, do you know what I'd like to be called?"

"I cannot imagine," said he.

"Well, I'd like to be called an Introducer. My friend, Mr. Blacksmith, let me introduce you to my friend, Mr. Plutocrat. I could almost swear that you were brothers, so near alike are you! You'll find each other wonderfully interesting once you get over the awkwardness of the introduction. And, Mr. White Man, let me present you particularly to my good friend, Mr. Negro. You will see if you sit down to it that this curious colour of the face is only skin deep."

"It's a good name!" said Mr. Vedder, laughing.

"It's a wonderful name," said I, "and it's about the biggest and finest work in the world — to know human beings just as they are, and to make them acquainted with one another just as they are. Why, it's the foundation of all the democracy there is, or ever will be. Sometimes I think that friendliness is the only achievement of life worth while — and unfriendliness the only tragedy."

I have since felt ashamed of myself when I thought how I lectured my unprotected host that day at luncheon; but it seemed to boil out of me irresistibly. The experiences of the past two days had stirred me to the very depths, and it seemed to me I must explain to somebody how it all impressed me — and to whom better than to my good friend Vedder?

As we were leaving the table an idea flashed across my mind which seemed, at first, so wonderful that it quite turned me dizzy.

"See here, Mr. Vedder," I exclaimed, "let me follow my occupation practically. I know Bill Hahn and I know you. Let me introduce you. If you could only get together, if you could only understand what good fellows you both are, it might go far toward solving these difficulties."

I had some trouble persuading him, but finally he consented, said he wanted to leave no stone unturned, and that he would meet Bill Hahn and some of the other leaders, if proper arrangements could be made.

I left him, therefore, in excitement, feeling that I was at the point of playing a part in a very great event. "Once get these men together," I thought, "and they *must* come to an understanding."

So I rushed out to the mill district, saying to myself over and over (I have smiled about it since!): "We'll settle this strike: we'll settle this strike: we'll settle this strike." After some searching I found my friend Bill in the little room over a saloon that served as strike headquarters. A dozen or more of the leaders were there, faintly distinguishable through clouds of tobacco smoke. Among them sat the great R —— D ——, his burly figure looming up at one end of the table, and his strong, rough, iron-jawed face turning first toward this speaker and then toward that. The discussion, which had evidently been lively, died down soon after I appeared at the door, and Bill Hahn came out to me and we sat down together in the adjoining room.

Here I broke eagerly into an account of the happenings of the day, described my chance meeting with Mr. Vedder — who was well known to Bill by reputation—and finally asked him squarely whether he would meet him. I think my enthusiasm quite carried him away.

"Sure, I will," said Bill Hahn heartily.

"When and where?" I asked, "and will any of the other men join you?"

Bill was all enthusiasm at once, for that was the essence of his temperament, but he said that he must first refer it to the committee. I waited, in a tense state of impatience, for what seemed to me a very long time; but finally the door opened and Bill Hahn came out bringing R —— D —— himself with him. We all sat down together, and R —— D —— began to ask questions (he was evidently suspicious as to who and what I was); but I think, after I talked with them for some time that I made them see the possibilities and the importance of such a meeting. I was greatly impressed with R —— D ——, the calmness and steadiness of the man, his evident shrewdness. "A real general," I said to myself. "I should like to know him better."

After a long talk they returned to the other room, closing the door behind them, and I waited again, still more impatiently.

It seems rather absurd now, but at that moment I felt firmly convinced that I was on the way to the permanent settlement of a struggle which had occupied the best brains of Kilburn for many weeks.

While I was waiting in that dingy ante-room, the other door slowly opened and a boy stuck his head in.

"Is David Grayson here?" he asked.

"Here he is," said I, greatly astonished that any one in Kilburn should be inquiring for me, or should know where I was.

The boy came in, looked at me with jolly round eyes for a moment, and dug a letter out of his pocket. I opened it at once, and glancing at the signature discovered that it was from Mr. Vedder.

"He said I'd probably find you at strike headquarters," remarked the boy.

This was the letter: marked "Confidential."

My Dear Grayson: I think you must be something of a hypnotist. After you left me I began to think of the project you mentioned, and I have talked it over with one or two of my associates. I would gladly hold this conference, but it does not now seem wise for us to do so. The interests we represent are too important to be jeopardized. In theory you are undoubtedly right, but in this case I think you will agree with me (when you think it over), we must not show any weakness. Come and stop with us to-night: Mrs. Vedder will be overjoyed to see you and we'll have another fine talk.

I confess I was a good deal cast down as I read this letter.

"What interests are so important?" I asked myself, "that they should keep friends apart?"

But I was given only a moment for reflection for the door opened and my friend Bill, together with R —— D —— and several other members of the committee, came out. I put the letter in my pocket, and for a moment my brain never worked under higher pressure. What should I say to them now? How could I explain myself?

Bill Hahn was evidently labouring under considerable excitement, but R —— D —— was as calm as a judge. He sat down in the chair opposite and said to me:

"We've been figuring out this proposition of Mr. Vedder's. Your idea is all right, and it would be a fine thing if we could really get together as you suggest upon terms of common understanding and friendship."

" Just what Mr. Vedder said, " I exclaimed.

"Yes," he continued, "it's all right in theory; but in this case it simply won't work. Don't you see it's got to be war? Your friend and I could probably understand each other — but this is a class war. It's all or nothing with us, and your friend Vedder knows it as well as we do."

After some further argument and explanation, I said:

"I see: and this is Socialism."

"Yes," said the great R——D——, "this is Socialism."

"And it's force you would use," I said.

"It's force *they* use," he replied.

After I left the strike headquarters that evening — for it was almost dark before I parted with the committee — I walked straight out through the crowded streets, so absorbed in my thoughts that I did not know in the least where I was going. The street lights came out, the crowds began to thin away, I heard a strident song from a phonograph at the entrance to a picture show, and as I passed again in front of the great, dark, many-windowed mill which had made my friend Vedder a rich man I saw a sentinel turn slowly at the corner. The light glinted on the steel of his bayonet. He had a fresh, fine, boyish face.

"We have some distance yet to go in this world," I said to myself, "no man need repine for lack of good work ahead."

It was only a little way beyond this mill that an incident occurred which occupied probably not ten minutes of time, and yet I have thought about it since I came home as much as I have thought about any other incident of my pilgrimage. I have thought how I might have acted differently under the circumstances, how I could have said this or how I ought to have done that — all, of course, now to no purpose whatever. But I shall not attempt to tell what I ought to have done or said, but what I actually did do and say on the spur of the moment.

It was in a narrow, dark street which opened off the brightly lighted main thorough-fare of that mill neighbourhood. A girl standing in the shadows between two build-ings said to me as I passed:

"Good evening."

I stopped instantly, it was such a pleasant, friendly voice.

"Good evening," I said, lifting my hat and wondering that there should be any one here in this back street who knew me.

"Where are you going?" she asked.

I stepped over quickly toward her, hat in hand. She was a mere slip of a girl, rather comely, I thought, with small childish features and a half-timid, half-bold look in her eyes. I could not remember having seen her before.

She smiled at me — and then I knew!

Well, if some one had struck me a brutal blow in the face I could not have been more astonished.

We know of things! — and yet how little we know until they are presented to us in concrete form. Just such a little school girl as I have seen a thousand times in the country, the pathetic childish curve of the chin, a small rebellious curl hanging low on her temple.

I could not say a word. The girl evidently saw in my face that something was the matter, for she turned and began to move quickly away. Such a wave of compassion (and anger, too) swept over me as I cannot well describe. I stepped after her and asked in a low voice:

"Do you work in the mills?"

"Yes, when there's work."

"What is your name?"

"Maggie —— "

"Well, Maggie," I said, "let's be friends."

She looked around at me curiously, questioningly.

"And friends," I said, "should know something about each other. You see I am a farmer from the country. I used to live in a city myself, a good many years ago, but I got tired and sick and hopeless. There was so much that was wrong about it. I tried to keep the pace and could not. I wish I could tell you what the country has done for me."

We were walking along slowly, side by side, the girl perfectly passive but glancing around at me from time to time with a wondering look. I don't know in the least now what prompted me to do it, but I began telling in a quiet, low voice — for, after all, she was only a child — I began telling her about our chickens at the farm and how Harriet had named them all, and one was

Frances E. Willard, and one, a speckled one, was Martha Washington, and I told her of the curious antics of Martha Washington and of the number of eggs she laid, and of the sweet new milk we had to drink, and the honey right out of our own hives, and of the things growing in the garden.

Once she smiled a little, and once she looked around at me with a curious, timid, half-wistful expression in her eyes.

"Maggie," I said, "I wish you could go to the country."

"I wish to God I could," she replied.

We walked for a moment in silence. My head was whirling with thoughts: again I had that feeling of helplessness, of inadequacy, which I had felt so sharply on the previous evening. What could I do?

When we reached the corner, I said:

"Maggie, I will see you safely home."

She laughed — a hard, bitter laugh.

"Oh, I don't need any one to show me around these streets!"

"I will see you home," I said.

So we walked quickly along the street together.

" We were walking along slowly, side by side "

"Here it is," she said finally, pointing to a dark, mean-looking, one-story house, set in a dingy, barren areaway.

"Well, good night, Maggie," I said, "and good luck to you."

"Good night," she said faintly.

When I had walked to the corner, I stopped and looked back. She was standing stock-still just where I had left her — a figure I shall never forget.

I have hesitated about telling of a further strange thing that happened to me that night — but have decided at last to put it in. I did not accept Mr. Vedder's invitation: I could not; but I returned to the room in the tenement where I had spent the previous night with Bill Hahn the Socialist. It was a small, dark, noisy room, but I was so weary that I fell almost immediately into a heavy sleep. An hour or more later — I don't know how long indeed — I was suddenly awakened and found myself sitting bolt upright in bed. It was close and dark and warm there in the room, and from without came the muffled sounds of the city. For an instant I waited, rigid with expectancy. And then I heard

as clearly and plainly as ever I heard anything:

"David! David!" in my sister Harriet's
voice.

It was exactly the voice in which she has
called me a thousand times. Without an
instant's hesitation, I stepped out of bed
and called out:

"I'm coming, Harriet! I'm coming!"

"What's the matter?" inquired Bill Hahn
sleepily.

"Nothing," I replied, and crept back into
bed.

It may have been the result of the strain
and excitement of the previous two days. I
don't explain it — I can only tell what
happened.

Before I went to sleep again I determined
to start straight for home in the morning:
and having decided, I turned over, drew a long,
comfortable breath and did not stir again, I
think, until long after the morning sun shone
in at the window.

THE RETURN

THE STORM

SHRIEK after shriek rose from the far shore,
I held more sweet than ... our own pain.
I walked from the ... holding onto the
open country — my pistols ... back in ...
in my throat, and the ... gold ... loud
straight before me. ...
I looked ... the flame and ...
and rested my eyes on the distant hills.

CHAPTER XII

THE RETURN

"Everything divine runs with light feet."

SURELY the chief delight of going away
from home is the joy of getting back again.
I shall never forget that spring morning when
I walked from the city of Kilburn into the
open country — my bag on my back, a song
in my throat, and the gray road stretching
straight before me. I remember how eagerly
I looked out across the fields and meadows
and rested my eyes upon the distant hills.

How roomy it all was! I looked up into the clear blue of the sky. There was space here to breathe, and distances in which the spirit might spread its wings. As the old prophet says, it was a place where a man might be placed alone in the midst of the earth.

I was strangely glad that morning of every little stream that ran under the bridges, I was glad of the trees I passed, glad of every bird and squirrel in the branches, glad of the cattle grazing in the fields, glad of the jolly boys I saw on their way to school with their dinner pails, glad of the bluff, red-faced teamster I met, and of the snug farmer who waved his hand at me and wished me a friendly good morning. It seemed to me that I liked every one I saw, and that every one liked me.

So I walked onward that morning nor ever have had such a sense of relief and escape, nor ever such a feeling of gayety.

"Here is where I belong," I said. "This is my own country. Those hills are mine, and all the fields, and the trees and the sky — and the road here belongs to me as much as it does to any one."

Coming presently to a small house near

the side of the road, I saw a woman working
with a trowel in her sunny garden. It was
good to see her turn over the warm brown soil;
it was good to see the plump green rows
of lettuce and the thin green rows of onions,
and the nasturtiums and sweet peas; it was
good — after so many days in that desert
of a city — to get a whiff of blossoming things.
I stood for a moment looking quietly over
the fence before the woman saw me. When
at last she turned and looked up, I said:

"Good morning."

She paused, trowel in hand.

"Good morning," she replied; "you look
happy."

I wasn't conscious that I was smiling out-
wardly.

"Well, I am," I said; "I'm going home."

"Then you *ought* to be happy," said she.

"And I'm glad to escape *that*," and I pointed
toward the city.

"What?"

"Why, that old monster lying there in the
valley."

I could see that she was surprised and even
a little alarmed. So I began intently to admire her young cabbages and comment on the

perfection of her geraniums. But I caught her eying me from time to time as I leaned there on the fence, and I knew that she would come back sooner or later to my remark about the monster. Having shocked your friend (not too unpleasantly), abide your time, and he will want to be shocked again. So I was not at all surprised to hear her ask:

"Have you travelled far?"

"I should *say* so!" I replied. "I've been on a very long journey. I've seen many strange sights and met many wonderful people."

"You may have been in California, then. I have a daughter in California."

"No," said I, "I was never in California."

"You've been a long time from home, you say?"

"A very long time from home."

"How long?"

"Three weeks."

"Three weeks! And how far did you say you had travelled?"

"At the farthest point, I should say sixty miles from home."

"But how can you say that in travelling only sixty miles and being gone three weeks that you have seen so many strange places and people?"

"Why," I exclaimed, "haven't you seen anything strange around here?"

"Why, no —— " glancing quickly around her.

"Well, I'm strange, am I not?"

"Well —— "

"And you're strange."

She looked at me with the utmost amazement. I could scarcely keep from laughing.

"I assure you," I said, "that if you travel a thousand miles you will find no one stranger than I am — or you are — nor anything more wonderful than all this —— " and I waved my hand.

This time she looked really alarmed, glancing quickly toward the house, so that I began to laugh.

"Madam," I said, "good morning!"

So I left her standing there by the fence looking after me, and I went on down the road.

"Well," I said, "she'll have something new to talk about. It may add a month to her life. Was there ever such an amusing world!"

About noon that day I had an adventure
that I have to laugh over every time I think
of it.   It was unusual, too, as being almost
the only incident of my journey which was
of itself in the least thrilling or out of the
ordinary.   Why, this might have made an
item in the country paper!

For the first time on my trip I saw a man
that I really felt like calling a tramp — a
tramp in the generally accepted sense of the
term.   When I left home I imagined I should
meet many tramps, and perhaps learn from
them odd and curious things about life; but
when I actually came into contact with the
shabby men of the road, I began to be puzzled.
What was a tramp, anyway?

I found them all strangely different, each
with his own distinctive history, and each
accounting for himself as logically as I could
for myself.   And save for the fact that in
none of them I met were the outward graces
and virtues too prominently displayed, I have
come back quite uncertain as to what a
scientist might call type-characteristics.   I
had thought of following Emerson in his
delightfully optimistic definition of a weed.
A weed, he says, is a plant whose virtues

have not been discovered. A tramp, then, is a man whose virtues have not been discovered. Or, I might follow my old friend the Professor (who dearly loves all growing things) in his even kindlier definition of a weed. He says that it is merely a plant misplaced. The virility of this definition has often impressed me when I have tried to grub the excellent and useful horseradish plants out of my asparagus bed! Let it be then — a tramp is a misplaced man, whose virtues have not been discovered.

Whether this is an adequate definition or not, it fitted admirably the man I overtook that morning on the road. He was certainly misplaced, and during my brief but exciting experience with him I discovered no virtues whatever.

In one way he was quite different from the traditional tramp. He walked with far too lively a step, too jauntily, and he had with him a small, shaggy, nondescript dog, a dog as shabby as he, trotting close at his heels. He carried a light stick, which he occasionally twirled over in his hand. As I drew nearer I could hear him whistling and even, from time to time, breaking into a lively bit of song. What a devil-may-care chap he seemed, anyway! I was greatly interested.

When at length I drew alongside he did not seem in the least surprised. He turned, glanced at me with his bold black eyes, and broke out again into the song he was singing. And these were the words of his song — at least, all I can remember of them:

> Oh, I'm so fine and gay,
> I'm so fine and gay,
> I have to take a dog along,
> To kape the ga-irls away.

What droll zest he put into it! He had a red nose, a globular red nose set on his face like an overgrown strawberry, and from under the worst derby hat in the world burst his thick curly hair.

"Oh, I'm so fine and gay," he sang, stepping to the rhythm of his song, and looking the very image of good-humoured impudence. I can't tell how amused and pleased I was — though if I had known what was to happen later I might not have been quite so friendly — yes, I would too!

We fell into conversation, and it wasn't long before I suggested that we stop for luncheon together somewhere along the road. He cast a quick appraising eye at my bag, and assented with alacrity. We climbed a fence and found a quiet spot near a little brook.

I was much astonished to observe the resources of my jovial companion. Although he carried neither bag nor pack and appeared to have nothing whatever in his pockets, he proceeded, like a professional prestidigitator, to produce from his shabby clothing an extraordinary number of curious things — a black tin can with a wire handle, a small box of matches, a soiled package which I soon learned contained tea, a miraculously big dry sausage wrapped in an old newspaper, and a clasp-knife. I watched him with breathless interest.

He cut a couple of crotched sticks to hang the pail on and in two or three minutes had a little fire, no larger than a man's hand, burning brightly under it. ("Big fires," said he wisely, "are not for us.") This he fed with dry twigs, and in a very few minutes he had a pot of tea from which he offered me the first drink. This, with my luncheon and part of his sausage, made up a very good meal.

While we were eating, the little dog sat sedately by the fire. From time to time his master would say, "Speak, Jimmy."

Jimmy would sit up on his haunches, his two front paws hanging limp, turn his head to one side in the drollest way imaginable and give a yelp. His master would toss him a bit of sausage or bread and he would catch it with a snap.

"Fine dog!" commented my companion.

"So he seems," said I.

After the meal was over my companion proceeded to produce other surprises from his pockets — a bag of tobacco, a brier pipe (which he kindly offered to me and which I kindly refused), and a soiled packet of cigarette papers. Having rolled a cigarette with practised facility, he leaned up against a tree, took off his hat, lighted the cigarette and, having taken a long draw at it, blew the smoke before him with an incredible air of satisfaction.

"Solid comfort this here — hey!" he exclaimed.

We had some further talk, but for so jovial a specimen he was surprisingly uncommunicative. Indeed, I think he soon decided that I somehow did not belong to the fraternity, that I was a "farmer" — in the most opprobrious sense — and he soon began to drowse, rousing himself once or twice to roll another cigarette, but finally dropping (apparently, at least) fast asleep.

I was glad enough of the rest and quiet after the strenuous experience of the last two days — and I, too, soon began to drowse. It didn't seem to me then that I lost consciousness at all, but I suppose I must have done so, for when I suddenly opened my eyes and sat up my companion had vanished. How he succeeded in gathering up his pail and packages so noiselessly and getting away so quickly is a mystery to me.

"Well," I said, "that's odd."

Rousing myself deliberately I put on my hat and was about to take up my bag when I suddenly discovered that it was open. My rain-cape was missing! It wasn't a very good rain-cape, but it was missing.

At first I was inclined to be angry, but when I thought of my jovial companion and the cunning way in which he had tricked me, I couldn't help laughing. At the same

time I jumped up quickly and ran down to
the road.

"I may get him yet," I said.

Just as I stepped out of the woods I
caught a glimpse of a man some hundreds
of yards away, turning quickly from the
main road into a lane or by-path. I wasn't
altogether sure that he was my man, but I
ran across the road and climbed the fence.
I had formed the plan instantly of cutting
across the field and so striking the by-road
farther up the hill. I had a curious sense of
amused exultation, the very spirit of the
chase, and my mind dwelt with the liveliest
excitement on what I should say or do if I
really caught that jolly spark of impudence.

So I came by way of a thicket along an
old stone fence to the by-road, and there,
sure enough, only a little way ahead of
me, was my man with the shaggy little
dog close at his heels. He was making
pretty good time, but I skirted swiftly
along the edge of the road until I had nearly
overtaken him. Then I slowed down to a
walk and stepped out into the middle of the
road. I confess my heart was pounding at a

lively rate. The next time he looked behind him — guiltily enough, too! — I said in the calmest voice I could command:

"Well, brother, you almost left me behind."

He stopped and I stepped up to him.

I wish I could describe the look in his face — mingled astonishment, fear, and defiance.

"My friend," I said, "I'm disappointed in you."

He made no reply.

"Yes, I'm disappointed. You did such a very poor job."

"Poor job!" he exclaimed.

"Yes," I said, and I slipped my bag off my shoulder and began to rummage inside. My companion watched me silently and suspiciously.

"You should not have left the rubbers."

With that I handed him my old rubbers. A peculiar expression came into the man's face.

"Say, pardner, what you drivin' at?"

"Well," I said, "I don't like to see such evidences of haste and inefficiency."

He stood staring at me helplessly, holding my old rubbers at arm's length.

"Come on now," I said, "that's over. We'll walk along together."

I was about to take his arm, but quick as a flash he dodged, cast both rubbers and rain-cape away from him, and ran down the road for all he was worth, the little dog, looking exactly like a rolling ball of fur, pelting after him. He never once glanced back, but ran for his life. I stood there and laughed until the tears came, and ever since then, at the thought of the expression on the jolly rover's face when I gave him my rubbers, I've had to smile. I put the rain-cape and rubbers back into my bag and turned again to the road.

Before the afternoon was nearly spent I found myself very tired, for my two days' experience in the city had been more exhausting for me, I think, than a whole month of hard labour on my farm. I found haven with a friendly farmer, whom I joined while he was driving his cows in from the pasture. I helped him with his milking both that night and the next morning, and found his situation and family most interesting — but I shall not here enlarge upon that experience.

It was late afternoon when I finally surmounted the hill from which I knew well enough I could catch the first glimpse of my farm. For a moment after I reached the top I could not raise my eyes, and when finally I was able to raise them I could not see.

"There is a spot in Arcady — a spot in Arcady — a spot in Arcady ——" So runs the old song.

There *is* a spot in Arcady, and at the centre of it there is a weather-worn old house, and not far away a perfect oak tree, and green fields all about, and a pleasant stream fringed with alders in the little valley. And out of the chimney into the sweet, still evening air rises the slow white smoke of the supper-fire.

I turned from the main road, and climbed the fence and walked across my upper field to the old wood lane. The air was heavy and sweet with clover blossoms, and along the fences I could see that the raspberry bushes were ripening their fruit.

So I came down the lane and heard the comfortable grunting of pigs in the pasture lot and saw the calves licking one another as they stood at the gate.

"How they've grown!" I said.

I stopped at the corner of the barn a moment. From within I heard the rattling of milk in a pail (a fine sound), and heard a man's voice saying:

"Whoa, there!   Stiddy now!"

"Dick's milking," I said.

So I stepped in at the doorway.

"Lord, Mr. Grayson!" exclaimed Dick, rising instantly and clasping my hand like a long-lost brother.

"I'm glad to see you!"

"I'm glad to see *you!*"

The warm smell of the new milk, the pleasant sound of animals stepping about in the stable, the old mare reaching her long head over the stanchion to welcome me, and nipping at my fingers when I rubbed her nose —

And there was the old house with the late sun upon it, the vines hanging green over the porch, Harriet's trim flower bed — I crept along quietly to the corner. The kitchen door stood open.

"Well, Harriet!" I said, stepping inside.

"Mercy!   David!"

"From within I heard the rattling of milk in a pail"

I have rarely known Harriet to be in quite such a reckless mood. She kept thinking of a new kind of sauce or jam for supper (I think there were seven, or were there twelve? on the table before I got through). And there was a new rhubarb pie such as only Harriet can make, just brown enough on top, and not too brown, with just the right sort of hills and hummocks in the crust, and here and there little sugary bubbles where a suggestion of the goodness came through —such a pie —— ! and such an appetite to go with it!

"Harriet," I said, "you're spoiling me. Haven't you heard how dangerous it is to set such a supper as this before a man who is perishing with hunger? Have you no mercy for me?"

This remark produced the most extraordinary effect. Harriet was at that moment standing in the corner near the pump. Her shoulders suddenly began to shake convulsively.

"She's so glad I'm home that she can't help laughing," I thought, which shows how penetrating I really am.

She was crying.

"Why, Harriet!" I exclaimed.

"Hungry!" she burst out, "and j-joking about it!"

I couldn't say a single word; something — it must have been a piece of the rhubarb pie — stuck in my throat. So I sat there and watched her moving quietly about in that immaculate kitchen. After a time I walked over to where she stood by the table and put my arm around her quickly. She half turned her head, in her quick, businesslike way. I noted how firm and clean and sweet her face was.

"Harriet," I said, "you grow younger every year."

No response.

"Harriet," I said, "I haven't seen a single person anywhere on my journey that I like as much as I do you."

The quick blood came up.

"There — there — David!" she said.

So I stepped away.

"And as for rhubarb pie, Harriet ——"

When I first came to my farm years ago there were mornings when I woke up with the strong impression that I had just been hearing the most exquisite music. I don't know whether this is at all a common experience, but in those days (and farther back in my early boyhood) I had it frequently. It did not seem exactly like music either, but was rather a sense of harmony, so wonderful, so pervasive that it cannot be described. I have not had it so often in recent years, but on the morning after I reached home it came to me as I awakened with a strange depth and sweetness. I lay for a moment there in my clean bed. The morning sun was up and coming in cheerfully through the vines at the window; a gentle breeze stirred the clean white curtains, and I could smell even there the odours of the garden.

I wish I had room to tell, but I cannot, of all the crowded experiences of that day — the renewal of acquaintance with the fields, the cattle, the fowls, the bees, of my long talks with Harriet and Dick Sheridan, who had cared for my work while I was away; of the wonderful visit of the Scotch Preacher, of Horace's shrewd and whimsical comments upon the general absurdity of the head of the Grayson family — oh, of a thousand things — and how when I went into my study and took up the nearest book in my favourite case — it chanced to be "The Bible in Spain" — it

opened of itself at one of my favourite pas-
sages, the one beginning:

"Mistos amande, I am content —— "

So it's all over! It has been a great experience; and it seems to me now that I have a
firmer grip on life, and a firmer trust in
that Power which orders the ages. In a
book I read not long ago, called "A Modern
Utopia," the writer provides in his imaginary
perfect state of society a class of leaders
known as Samurai. And, from time to
time, it is the custom of these Samurai to
cut themselves loose from the crowding
world of men, and with packs on their backs
go away alone to far places in the deserts or
on Arctic ice caps. I am convinced that
every man needs some such change as this,
an opportunity to think things out, to get a
new grip on life, and a new hold on God. But
not for me the Arctic ice cap or the desert!
I choose the Friendly Road — and all the common people who travel in it or live along it —
I choose even the busy city at the end of it.

I assure you, friend, that it is a wonderful
thing for a man to cast himself freely for a
time upon the world, not knowing where his

next meal is coming from, nor where he is going to sleep for the night. It is a surprising readjuster of values. I paid my way, I think, throughout my pilgrimage; but I discovered that stamped metal is far from being the world's only true coin. As a matter of fact, there are many things that men prize more highly — because they are rarer and more precious.

My friend, if you should chance yourself some day to follow the Friendly Road, you may catch a fleeting glimpse of a man in a rusty hat, carrying a gray bag, and sometimes humming a little song under his breath for the joy of being there. And it may actually happen, if you stop him, that he will take a tin whistle from his bag and play for you, "Money Musk," or "Old Dan Tucker," or he may produce a battered old volume of Montaigne from which he will read you a passage. If such an adventure should befall you, know that you have met

Your friend,

DAVID GRAYSON.

P. S. — Harriet bemoans most of all the unsolved mystery of the sign man. But

it doesn't bother me in the least. I'm
glad now I never found him. The poet
sings his song and goes his way. If we sought
him out how horribly disappointed we might
be! We might find him shaving, or eating
sausage, or drinking a bottle of beer. We
might find him shaggy and unkempt where
we imagined him beautiful, weak where we
thought him strong, dull where we thought
him brilliant. Take then the vintage of his
heart and let him go. As for me, I'm glad
some mystery is left in this world. A thousand signs on my roadways are still as un-
explainable, as mysterious, and as beguiling
as this. And I can close my narrative with
no better motto for tired spirits than that of
the country roadside:

REST

THE COUNTRY LIFE PRESS
GARDEN CITY, N. Y.